To R. S. Shaw, President,
M.S.C. with best regards.

Clements C. Fry
June (93)

THE ANATOMY

OF PERSONALITY

BY HOWARD W. HAGGARD

*

THE SCIENCE OF HEALTH AND DISEASE

DEVILS, DRUGS, AND DOCTORS

THE LAME, THE HALT, AND THE BLIND

*

Harper & Brothers

Publishers

HYPOCHONDRIAC

The ANATOMY *of* PERSONALITY

By CLEMENTS C. FRY, M.D.
Associate Professor of Psychiatry and Mental Hygiene, Yale University,

and HOWARD W. HAGGARD, M.D.
Associate Professor of Applied Physiology, Yale University.

ILLUSTRATED

HARPER *&* BROTHERS *Publishers*

NEW YORK *and* LONDON

1936

Contents

Preface   ix

PART I

Chapter 1. The Manners of All Men   3

II

Chapter 2. Realities that Lie in the Flesh   33

III

Chapter 3. Freedom that Grows with the
            Mind   77

IV

Chapter 4. Bondage in Moods and Emotions 129
Chapter 5. Bondage in Moods and Emotions
            (continued)   173

V

Chapter 6. The Meek, the Mild, the Militant 215
Chapter 7. The Meek, the Mild, the Militant
            (continued)   253

VI

Chapter 8. The Streams of Life   303
Index   351

LIST OF ILLUSTRATIONS

HYPOCHONDRIAC   *Frontispiece*

                                                      PAGE
THE IMPURE MAN   5

A FACE OF THE "LONG EGG-SHAPE"   47

A FACE OF THE "SHORT EGG-SHAPE"   53

A FACE OF THE GENERAL PYKNIC TYPE   59

A FACE OF THE EXTREME PYKNIC TYPE—"BROAD SHIELD-
    SHAPE"   65

THE SUSPICIOUS MAN   149

THE FEARFUL MAN   191

THE SOPHIST   237

MARIE CARTERI   339

Preface

WE HAVE attempted to present, shorn of the technicalities of psychiatry, what is essentially a concept for the structural analysis of personality. It is our hope that our reader will obtain from it the insight into his own personality that gives the understanding of self which is the first step toward self-improvement; and also the insight into the peculiarities of others which is the first step toward the broad tolerance that gives respect for fellow men.

We have derived our material from many sources, but we have made no citations except in the case of direct quotations. If we have not mentioned specifically the names of Freud, Jung, Adler, Kretchmer, Meyer, Schneider, Kahn, and many others, it is not because we are of different "schools." We have taken from each what suited our needs and purposes and adapted it to our own point of view. Often the words of the "masters" have not been revered as gospel, but the acknowledgment of our debt is none the less real.

There is, however, one source to which we owe an especial acknowledgment. With the generous permission of the author, Dr. Eugene Kahn, Sterling Professor of Psychiatry and Mental Hygiene at Yale University, we have drawn heavily upon his *Psychopathic Personalities.** In this work Dr. Kahn has presented primarily for the medical profession a new and highly valuable conception of the abnormalities of personality. His classification is based upon deviations occurring in impulse, temperament, and character. It will be noted by those who are familiar with his works that in Parts IV, V, and VI of our book we follow closely the outline of his classification. We differ in terminology, in certain definitions—notably that of character—and in point of view.

That we have followed a presentation dealing wholly with psychopathic personalities does not signify that our interest is in the abnormal. The personality of the average, and therefore presumably normal, man has the same structural constituents as that of the most extreme psychopath. The average man shows fewer deviations in the qualities of these constituents than does the man whom the psychiatrist would class as definitely abnormal. But he nevertheless shows deviations. The distinction is, we believe, one only of degree. And yet we believe in the normal man, we have written for him

* Yale University Press, 1931.

[x]

and about him. But always to us he remains the average man—one who is neither a misfit in the environment of our society nor yet, equally abnormal, a genius. If in our view of mankind we appear perhaps on the side of the Quaker—"All the world is daft save only thee and me and thee art a little queer"—it is because in our experience we have found few men who show personalities so neutral as to be free from all distinguishing peculiarities.

THE AUTHORS

THE ANATOMY

OF PERSONALITY

PART I

THE MANNERS OF ALL MEN

Chapter I

THE MANNERS OF ALL MEN

IN THE ninety-ninth year of a life rich in the observation of men, Theophrastus, the pupil of Plato and friend of Aristotle, wrote his book of characters.

First he states, as it were, his qualifications as an authority on human behavior. They are the common, but not especially valid, ones of age and experience. "I have thought myself fitted," he says, "for the task of describing those habitual peculiarities by which the manners of everyone are distinguished."

And then he raises a question—the very crux of his whole problem: Why do these peculiarities exist? "I have always been perplexed," he admits, "when I have endeavored to account for the fact that among a people who, like the Greeks, inhabit the same climate and are reared under the same system of education, there should prevail so great a diversity of manners." He finds no answer to the question, and so he merely describes men as *he* sees them in the surroundings of ancient

Greece. With incisive phrases he delineates the predominant characteristics in the behavior of thirty different types. Here is his description of the so-called "impure man," or as we should say, vulgarian.

"This man is everywhere to be known by the open and scandalous grossness of his manners; he willfully offends the eye of modesty. At the theatre it is his delight to clap his hands after the rest of the audience is still, and to hiss the actors whom others applaud; and in an interval of silence he belches so loud as to attract the notice of all about him. He frequents the fruit stalls in the open market, from which he helps himself; munching nuts, apples, or almonds while he feigns to chat with the vendor. He calls to some one by his name, in public, with whom he has no acquaintance; or commands a person to wait for him whom he perceives to be hastening on business. He will accost a man with mock congratulations who is leaving court after having lost a case, and incurred a heavy fine. As he returns from market, laden with eatables, he hires musicians, displays what he has bought to all he may meet, and invites them to the revel; or, standing at a shop or tavern door, he proclaims that he is about to get drunk. He will wish ill luck to his mother as he sees her going to consult the augur. He overthrows

THE IMPURE MAN

"Standing at a tavern door, he proclaims that he is
about to get drunk."
*From the English translation of the "Characters"
of Theophrastus*

the cup of the worshippers who are about to perform their libations; and then stares and grins as if the accident were portentous. If a female performer is playing on a musical instrument, first he claps while others would fain to listen; then thrums the tune; and presently rudely commands her to be silent. At supper he heedlessly spits across the table on the servant."

The behavior of the "characters" that Theophrastus describes—even that of the "impure man"—could be recognized among the men we encounter today. Human nature, and the gamut of human behavior, have not changed in 2,300 years. Personality, the basis of human behavior, is inborn in the species *homo sapiens* just as is the physical form, the physique. The two characterize man mentally and physically; they establish him as a man; they differentiate him from all other animals.

The configuration of the body exhibits considerable variation within the range that is still recognizable as human. Men differ from one another in the details of their physical appearance. Consequently they are recognizable as individuals; they can be classified on the basis of their physical peculiarities as tall or short, dark or light, and so on to a multitude of details.

Likewise, men differ in the traits of their personalities. They have individual peculiarities which distinguish them, which afford a basis upon which it is possible to evaluate them.

The basic traits of personality which mark one man from another and set off each as an individual are as fixed and permanent throughout life as are physical peculiarities. Theophrastus and his many successors who have characterized men could not have portrayed types if such were not the case—if the vulgarian became the "busybody," and the "busybody" in turn became the "morose." Instead, each individual is born with certain fixed traits of personality which establish his individuality and dominate his behavior.

Although the classification of men that Theophrastus made was, as will be seen, fallacious in many respects, it nevertheless set a mode for classification. His characters attracted much interest; his book has been translated into many languages; it has been published in many editions. Men have always wanted to know the peculiarities of other men. They still do. But why? The answer in part is to be found in the kind of characters that Theophrastus chose to present. Each of the thirty types exhibits behavior which is unpleasant to most of us—the ruffian, the garrulous, the shameless, the impure, the petulant, the old trifler.

All of the characters Theophrastus describes behaved in a manner that tended to undermine the principles by which he regulated his life. They thus threatened his integrity and his security. Is that not one of the reasons why we are all interested in understanding the behavior of others? Our interest is self-centered. To maintain our own integrity, our own security, and to allow our own development, we must know the peculiarities that distinguish the men with whom we are brought into contact or with whom our interests may come into conflict. We must discover the evil intentions of the dissembler, discount the words of the adulator, see through the false logic of the plausible, avoid contagion from the shameless and injury from the ruffian, and prevent the ostentatious from imposing upon us. We must not be exploited by others; must not be "taken in" and so be deprived of our own values. But understanding the peculiarities of others is only half—or even less than half—of the problem of maintaining our integrity and security, and permitting our own self-development. Only a few of the situations that confront us involve the personalities of others; but our own personality underlies every situation. Its peculiarities dominate our own behavior.

What, then, are its peculiarities; how do they benefit or interfere with the accomplishment of our aims and purposes; how do they affect other people? Most of us appear eager to know the answers to these questions—sometimes pitifully eager for self-understanding. But do we really want to know?

It is far more difficult to know oneself than to know others, for we are prejudiced. And, above all, we do not wish to know the full truth about ourselves. We reject it passionately when it is told to us; when we find that in the eyes of others the estimates of our personality are contrary to our own desires and delusions. Is it wise, is it even safe, for a man to know his own personality with too much understanding? Would it be better for him to carry on in ignorance rather than uncover unpleasant things? Or will it give him confidence and depth of understanding? The answers to these questions depend upon the type of personality and upon its ability to meet facts with courage. To the brave and philosophical man nothing can be of more benefit than knowledge of self. It is he who says: "I am what I am. I will take such qualities as I have and do with them what I can." With such an attitude of honesty and courage, knowledge of self begets confidence, peace, and comfort.

Each one of us evaluates consciously or unconsciously everyone with whom he comes in contact. We also try

to evaluate ourselves. And so, unlike Theophrastus and
his many successors, in describing types of behavior,
we deal not only with extreme and unpleasant characters, but with the "average man" as well—the man
whom we meet daily, the man whom we call friend, or
enemy, or mere acquaintance. And the man whom we
employ, or who employs us.

Is it possible, by the descriptive method used by
Theophrastus, by knowing types of behavior, to make
a valid estimate of human personalities? It is not. The
method—and it is the common method of evaluating
oneself and others—is fallacious for many reasons. Like
Theophrastus, few if any of us are unprejudiced observers. Like him, we tend to compare men—ourselves
as well—to some standard of behavior that seems desirable or undesirable to us. When one reads all the
sketches from Theophrastus, he has obtained not so
much a view of human types as a view of the author
himself, his standards of social conventions, his moral
ideals and his personal likes and dislikes.

Standards at best are mere conventions. They have
scant basis in raw human nature; and it is raw human
nature that in the last analysis dictates human behavior.
If we are asked to describe a good man, one with whom
we feel secure, the diversity of our answers will show

that we hold not one standard of judgment, but many. By the bigoted person, men are judged on the basis of whether or not they adhere to his faith and his sect, believe in his god, support his realm of security. They become "bad" simply by disagreeing with him in belief. To the banker, honesty is a standard; and to the bon vivant, warmth, and companionship, and geniality. Even the "impure man" whom Theophrastus held up to contempt no doubt had his set of standards. If he could have been coerced from his display of ego-centricities on the street, at the theater, and at the table long enough to write a book of "characters" from his own point of view, it would be as illuminating as that of Theophrastus. And no doubt the "impure man" could find a place in it for Theophrastus, under the title of Miss Prissy, or the prig, or the meddlesome ass. Who knows but that he might be right in his opinion?

So-called "character types" such as Theophrastus drew cannot serve as a guide to the knowledge of men unless we are all agreed on one set standard of behavior, unless we all have the same concept of morals, the same likes and dislikes as the author of the sketches.

Such attempts at "knowledge of men" are from the beginning doomed to failure. They are doomed as completely as would be attempts to classify human physiques on the basis of the clothing worn by men and a comparison of their style to some standard that pleased the author. That is precisely what Theophrastus did in describing his types of men. He classified the externals—the costumes, so to speak, in which their behavior appeared on the streets of Athens. What he was dealing with was characters, but not personalities.

Human character, unlike personality, is not inborn. It is acquired. *Character is a product resulting from the action of the environment upon the personality. The adaptation of the personality, the conditioning of its inherent qualities, thus results in patterns of reaction and modes of behavior, which in time become the character.* Character as thus formed then guides behavior. But the acquisition of character does not alter the fundamental qualities of the personality itself; it determines the forms in which they are displayed. The shape that the individual's character assumes is not dictated solely by environment; character can be shaped only within the limits of the inherent qualities of the particular personality. In spite of all influences of environment, personality retains its identity. It is the raw material upon which the environment acts in shaping character. But in the product the material unaltered is not only present, but is shown. It is the man himself. Theophrastus in describing characters, therefore, dealt with a composite. He was not revealing the peculiarities of men, but merely the behavior that some personalities show when placed in a definite environment. He judged the man and the environment together. We are here concerned primarily with the personality itself.

The basic qualities of personality are inborn, unchanging; they are a part of the human constitution. They are the same in any environment, in all environments. But character lies between the personality and the environment and is therefore influenced by both— one unchanging and the other variable to the full extent of human experience. Character is personality modified by the individual's particular environment; the "manners of the man" are formed correspondingly. But in spite of all environmental influences, personality—and that is our one chief interest here—remains unaltered.

It is difficult, indeed impossible at a single stroke, to discard environment and to strip off character, to see beneath the naked personality standing there in its entirety. The approach to the personality must be indirect, for the personality is revealed only through behavior. But behavior can be seen; environment can be seen. They are two visible variables; there is only one constant—personality; but all three are related.

The situation is almost a mathematical problem; there are axioms: When the personality is known and the environment is known, it is possible to predict with reasonable accuracy the behavior. And conversely—and this is the point of paramount importance—when the behavior is known and the environment is known, it is possible to evaluate the personality. It would be satisfying to be able to conclude in the manner of the mathematician: "the personality, Q.E.D."

But the apparent simplicity of the problem is marred by an additional fact: a man not only presents his personality to the world for the judgment of others, but he also sees the world and judges others through his own personality. None of us can escape this fact: a personality judged by a personality. No man ever learns about himself completely; no one ever becomes a wholly dispassionate observer of other personalities.

There is, however, a way around the difficulty. The intact personality with its acquired character represents the man with a complete and complicated mode of behavior, a set of preconceived ideas, prejudices, and patterns of comparison. In examining this complex totality our emotions are touched and our judgment correspondingly perverted. But the component elements of personality, separated from the whole, do not so affect

[15]

us. They appear as mere abstractions. In this abstract manner we can study ourselves and others much as a chemist analyzes a mineral in order to determine its components.

Before this analytical method came into use in natural science, there was only a descriptive method of classifying mineral substances. Each known substance was identified by the impressions it made upon the senses of the individual observer; it was recognized by its appearance and texture, its taste and smell—in short, the character it presented. The method was analogous to the descriptive method applied by Theophrastus to the classification of men.

Modern chemistry brought order and system into the field and supplied a sound basis for classification by showing that there are only a few fundamental elements by the combination of which all matter is formed. The differences in the properties of the various materials arise from the peculiarities of the component elements entering into each particular substance, their number and their arrangement. Thus it became possible to replace long and uncertain descriptions based on sensory impressions by a concise formula that expresses the ultimate nature of the substance; one that reveals its reactions, and the character of its behavior, in any situation. The mere statement of the fact that table salt is a combination of equal parts of the two elements, sodium and chlorine—sodium chloride—is far more precise and revealing, far more identifying, than is a long description based upon its physical appearance.

Modern psychiatry supplies a similar approach to the classification of human personalities. It is the method of structural analysis—but it is not to be confused with psychoanalysis.

Human personality may be analyzed into a few basic elements. Every personality contains each of these elements in some degree. They are arranged, not haphazardly, but always in the same relation to each other. The personality as a whole has a definite structure. But the elements constituting it may vary in quality and quantity. Among individual personalities the range of these variations is great. No two personalities are precisely alike. It thus becomes possible with a brief statement of the peculiarities of the basic components of any personality to define the personality and to characterize its type of behavior in any environment. In short, the man himself is revealed.

The basic elements into which personality is divided for the sake of analysis are five in number:

(1) The physique.

(2) The impulse or driving force.

(3) The intelligence.

(4) The temperament.

(5) The ego.

The details of each of these elements, their variations, the way in which they are recognized, and their separate influences upon behavior will be the subjects of subsequent chapters.

Here, purely for the sake of setting forth some of the more general aspects of the structural analysis of personality, the method, shorn of all details, will be applied to the "impure man" as far as Theophrastus's description of his behavior in the environment of ancient Athens will allow.

The striking fact uncovered is that this man, for all of his grossness, offensiveness, and unproductiveness, has a strong and not a weak personality. He has qualities which, in a different environment, might have allowed him to acquire the character of a "good citizen"—even that of a leader in civic matters, an upholder of the church. But there are inherent limits to the "goodness" that could be attained by this personality; definite and permanent limits. He might become a good

[18]

citizen of only one type—one whom we might respect and fear, but never love.

Theophrastus has left many gaps in his description of the "impure man;" he has told us nothing concerning his physique. And, as will be seen in the next chapter, there is an association between physique and certain general tendencies of the personality. It is not an exact association, but it affords a ready clue to the direction of certain traits of personality. Men with a short and stocky physique—we shall call it the pyknic physique in the next chapter—usually have a greater hold upon the realities of life, a better understanding and appreciation of men and material things, than do tall and slender individuals, whom in turn we shall later define as possessing the leptosomic physique.

Theophrastus has not told us whether the "impure man" is short and stocky, or tall and thin, or of some intermediate build. But one thing bearing upon physique he has told us: unmistakably the personality of this man tends toward the realities of life; his outlook upon the world is materialistic. In the character with which this man is presented the realities that appeal are sensual ones. But his pleasures are not enjoyed alone; he wants contact with other men. "As he returns from the market, laden with eatables, he hires musicians, displays what he has bought to all he may meet and invites them to the revel." Indeed, one of the complaints that Theophrastus makes against him is that he is constantly to be found where men gather. He offends their sight, on the street, at the theater, in the temple. If he were seclusive, his offensiveness would not concern Theophrastus. His outlook upon religion is a material one; he does not seek the support of a deity; he pokes fun at the worshipers. Here is a personality that deals with tangible things, not with ideology. This personality would never in any environment allow its possessor to be a romantic spirit, a gentle lover, a writer of sentimental poems, a technical jurist, a metaphysicist, or even a fanatic. In the guise of any character, in any environment, his personality is that of a practical, aggressive realist.

It is difficult to conceive of this man as being of leptosomic physique, to imagine him with a slender frame, a flat chest, a long neck, and an egg-shaped face. The reader, if he pauses to speculate on his probable physique, must invariably think of him as bulky, gross in outline, bull-necked, round-headed. The artist who drew the illustrations for the English translation of the "Characters" of Theophrastus made him stocky, barrel-shaped, short-necked—the typical pyknic physique—but in this case with flabby mouth and swollen nose, indications of his excesses in the rôle that he plays as the "impure man."

The second component of personality, the impulse, the basic biological urge, the driving force, is strong in this personality. Here is no shy and shrinking debauchee, no "feeble soul," but an aggressive, virile man. The results of his aggression may not be acceptable from the viewpoint of cultured standards of behavior, but the character of the product does not alter the fact of the aggression. In any environment, in any walk of life, this personality would maintain its strength.

The third component, the degree of intelligence inherent in this personality, we cannot judge. The natural inclination, dictated by our dislike of him in the character in which we see him, is to say he is stupid. But that is a biased inference, for we lack the evidence. For the sake of further discussion, we shall make an assumption (bearing in mind that this is merely an argumentative analysis rather than a real one); assumptions cannot be made in correctly evaluating living men. But we shall assume that the "impure man" has average intelligence, or, since that is almost a circumlocution for stupidity, slightly better than average intelligence.

There is at least nothing in the description of Theophrastus that forbids this assumption.

The fourth component of personality, temperament, again cannot be evaluated in the full scope of its qualities—its moods, its tempo, its reactiveness, its resonance. But certainly its tempo is quick, not phlegmatic. This man does not sit in sodden silence at the tavern bench, slowly and indifferently drinking from his flagon. Instead, "standing at the shop or tavern door, he proclaims that he is about to get drunk." He calls to men on the streets; he applauds at the theater; he hisses; he is violent, almost explosive. His misdirected energies flow into a thousand channels of activity.

With another character the energies of this personality, its activity, even its quarrelsomeness, might have been directed into productive channels. As a business man he might find an outlet for his quarrelsomeness in commercial competition. But in any environment this is not an easy temperament for those who are brought in contact with it. Subordinates suffer, and so do wife and children. Aggressive, active, explosive, irritable, no environment can change these qualities; it can only direct them to more productive ends than those appearing in the "impure man."

The final quality of his temperament is coldness

toward others, a lack of sympathy and appreciation. It is not warm and responsive. The "impure man" is even aggressive in his coldness: "he will accost a man with mock congratulations who is leaving court after having lost a case and incurred a heavy fine. He wishes ill-luck to his mother as he sees her going to consult the augur." He has no sympathy for the actor he hisses, or for the audience he disturbs. He has no remorse. A different environment might have shaped from this personality a character with a sense of justice and respect for the rights of others, but never a feeling of sympathy and depth of understanding. He would, then, be honest and tactful in his dealings, not for fear of wronging others, but because it paid; and in his business relations he would employ a good lawyer to point out the tenuous line between legal honesty and dishonesty. The tears of widows and orphans would not touch his soul; he could discharge his aging, faithful employees summarily—"for business is business." No gentle acts of charity emanate from such a personality in any character that it might acquire; if charity were indicated, it would be duly advertised and given only for value received.

It is the coldness in this personality that gives it ruthlessness rather than mere aggression. When combined with sufficient intelligence its possessor could, in the environment of commerce, rise to high position, might even receive public respect and be held up as an emulative example of a successful man. In a military career the ruthlessness would have undoubted advantages.

With warmth substituted for coldness quite a different personality would emerge. It would no longer be the personality that the "impure man" possessed. With warmth, the personality would have inherently depth of feeling and understanding of others. With all other qualities except the coldness unchanged, this personality in the field of commerce, instead of yielding a ruthless man, might give one of the most lovable—the gruff but kind-hearted man, with much bark and little bite; an aggression softened with kindness; a man who to outsiders appeared formidable, but to whom every employee and associate was loyal. In the home he would be the "bad boy" type of husband, tactless, exploding at restraints and trivialities, but immediately clumsily contrite, loved by his wife and adored by his children.

But the "impure man" did not contain this saving quality of warmth in his personality. He was born cold and ruthless, and cold and ruthless he would remain in any environment.

The final component of personality, ego, involves all of the peculiarities of strength and direction of self-regard. And in the "impure man" there is a peculiarity of ego that stands out from all the other qualities of his personality and would give color to any character he acquired. It is his egocentricity. Here is a man who thinks that he is important, who overvalues himself, but who is at the same time insecure in his overvaluation. Others must continually be made conscious of his presence and react to it. The true egoist is quite a different type; his aim is power, not prestige. He is as indifferent to the regard as he is to the opinion of others; he does not need to have his self-estimate confirmed by a show of attention. But the egocentric lacks this ego independence; he needs the attention of others. Often he cares not how he gains it. It is not the quality of the attention he seeks, but attention itself. He must have prestige, even false prestige, though to obtain it he is forced to "offend the eye of modesty." To him attention of any kind, for any cause, is better than disregard. Disregarded, he would only increase his efforts to obtain attention; ignored, he would break all conventions, be violent even to obtain attention—prestige. Consequently, as Theophrastus tells us, the "impure man" clapped his hands after the rest of the audience was still; hissed the actors whom the others applauded; even belched loudly to attract the attention of those about him. The theater, the restaurant, and the drawing-room—in short, among the crowd and never in private—that is where the egocentric exploits his peculiarity. There must be an audience. Most egocentrics feel some restraint of conventions; they merely laugh too loud, or applaud too loud, or call the waiter ostentatiously, but here is an aggressive, unrestrained egocentric. When the performer at the theater held attention by her musical efforts, he first sulked and then, unable to bear being deprived of his attention any longer, he rudely commanded her to be silent.

Certainly the product of his egocentricity is vulgarity, and it was this vulgarity that caught and held the attention of Theophrastus. But vulgarity is no ingredient of personality. It resulted here, as it often does elsewhere, merely from the display of egocentricity in the particular environment in which this man found himself. In a less refined environment his habits might not be called vulgar. Vulgarity is primarily a matter of social standards.

In our analysis of the personality of the "impure man" we have gleaned the peculiarities of three of its basic components: the impulse is strong, the temperament is active but cold, and the ego is overvalued but insecurely so—egocentric. We have endowed him with a reasonable intelligence and made the assumption that he is of pyknic physique. Such is the actual unchanging man, the personality, freed from all influence of environment, stripped bare of all acquired character.

From this knowledge of a personality its general reactions can be predicted for any situation, for any environment. And so merely for the sake of further, and purely argumentative, presentation, let us move this synthetic product to some other environment. Let us take it from the streets of ancient Athens—no doubt to the relief of the Athenians—and reincarnate it in an army on campaign. The result—there can be no other—is an aggressive, active, cold, and ruthless warrior with an overwhelming desire to attract attention. Certainly such a man would be the detestation of his officers and of most of his equals. Under any circumstances he would be a barrack-room nuisance, probably a bully, but always a storm center. But may not these same ingredients also yield a hero? The goal sought in heroism would not be love of companions or country. It would be the desire to win prestige, to "show off." If opportunity offered, he would achieve heroism in striving for this goal as well as for any other. But it would have to be heroism before a crowd; never would he risk his life without assurance of certain reward—the reward of attention and applause. One can see him there standing before the ranks to receive his decoration, slyly grimacing for the amusement of his companions as the general pins the medal on his jacket. For the true egocentric no straw of attention is too small to be left ungleaned! And in the barracks among his companions he disdains congratulations and throws his medal aside as if it were a mere nothing. This action attracts still more attention, and what is always a source of satisfaction to the egocentric, it belittles all others who have been decorated for heroism. It sets him above them. It is this phase of the behavior of the egocentric that marks those whom we call destructive critics. They belittle their fellow men for their own aggrandizement.

To the public who hear and read of his acts of heroism, this man is a hero. It is the result he achieves and not the purpose he has in achieving it, that is the standard his actions are judged by. The public, hearing of his acts, do not know the quality of his personality that motivated his "heroism," any more than Theophrastus recognized that this same quality motivated his vulgarity as the "impure man" on the streets of Athens.

But to those who can evaluate personality, this man is neither a vulgarian nor a hero—he is merely an egocentric with a strong impulse, and a cold and active temperament.

What might these qualities yield on still another stage —the commercial one this time? Precisely these qualities of personality have yielded men who, if successful in their ventures, have been much admired, much head-lined, much feared, and much hated "giants of finance." To the personality with which we deal the prestige of ruthless conquest in the market would not wholly sat-isfy the needs of his egocentricity. His behavior might take the shape, strange as it may seem, of avoiding publicity, forcibly throwing out the newspaper report-ers who sought interviews. Often more attention is attracted by this means than by appearing to seek publicity. More probably the "showing off" would be along the more direct line of ostentation—the house that cost a fabulous sum, but was occupied only occa-sionally; the enormous staff of servants; the special auto-mobiles; the police escort; the bizarre and extravagant banquets.

A description of such a "type" written after the man-ner of Theophrastus would bear no resemblance what-ever to the "impure man." The two would never be recognized as the same personality merely in different surroundings. But those who followed the analytical method of studying personality would see that but for the grace of environment this financier, and that hero as well, are reincarnations of the "impure man" who once walked upon the streets of Athens and offended the eyes and ears of Theophrastus—a personality with a strong impulse, a cold, but active temperament, and marked egocentricity.

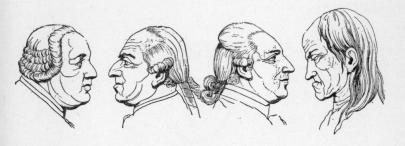

PART II

REALITIES THAT LIE IN THE FLESH

Chapter II

REALITIES THAT LIE IN THE FLESH

I T IS a traditional belief that "character" can be read in the face and "temperament" in the form; it is also a fallacious belief. But it is one to which many people, even today, subscribe wholeheartedly. Such attempts at "character-reading" rank with phrenology, the study of the "bumps" on the head. Estimates of personality traits based on such qualities as the tilt of the nose for indecision, the squareness of the chin for determination, or the height of the forehead for intellect are as absurd as attempts to predict the probability of appendicitis, gall stones, or cancer on the basis of these same peculiarities. Yet such absurdities are frequently accepted by otherwise intelligent people. These fallacious beliefs find their way into the practices of employment offices, the training of salesmen, even into social relations. There is no rule of thumb in measuring men, no short cut to the understanding of personality.

Yet when we have done scoffing at all of the fanciful

attempts to classify personality according to physique, we can not escape the stubborn fact that some relation does exist. And it appears, moreover, to exist not alone in clearly marked traits of personality, but also in the predisposition to certain physical diseases.

Caricaturists through the ages have drawn the prototypes of personality in face and figure. They are familiar at a glance; no legend is needed to tell which is the flighty, talkative lady; the harsh father; the grouch; the explosive colonel; the garrulous neighbor; the timid soul; the irritable husband; and the genial Santa Claus.

In literature and drama certain physical types are definitely associated with certain traits of personality. If one doubts this fact, try to imagine a Hamlet with the physical characteristics of a Falstaff!

Shakespeare in "Julius Cæsar" expresses the popular belief in the association of character and physique in the lines:

Cæsar: "Let me have men about me that are fat;
Sleek-headed men, and such as sleep o' nights;
Yond' Cassius hath a lean and hungry look;
He thinks too much; such men are dangerous."

Antony: "Fear him not, Cæsar; he is not dangerous;
He is a noble Roman and well given."

Cæsar: "Would he were fatter! . . ."

The association of racial types and racial temperaments affords still another field for thought on the relation between physique and personality. Here the caricaturists have given us John Bull, stocky, muscular, short of leg and arm, bluff and hearty, a good fellow well met. Fritz, the German, is fat and rotund, genial, convivial, a lover of groups in singing fests and drinking bouts. Alfonso and Giuseppe, the Latins, are also short and fat, and they are voluble and excitable, demonstrative in mood and motion. The melancholy Dane, however, is tall and lean, quiet and self-centered, morose and irritable. Uncle Sam is tall and angular, shrewdly calculating, not a good mixer. His prototype was not in the hospitable Southern planters, but in the dour Puritans, a group that could not "get along" in the mother country and separated so that they could be by themselves.

Certainly there seems to be an element of justification for the popular view that among fat men are to be found a greater proportion of kindly and jovial souls, while the seclusive, the cold, and the calculating are found more often among the thin. But it is even more certain that the sweeping conclusion cannot be drawn that all fat men are kind and jovial and all thin men seclusive, cold, and calculating. Common observations indicate the contrary. There have been brutal, heartless gangsters, possessed of a physique that would delight any group of children on Christmas Eve; and there have been thin and wizened men whose every act was one of kindly generosity and self-sacrifice.

It is a far cry from beliefs based on general impressions to facts founded on scientific observation. It is even possible that characterizations in cartoon, drama, and literature are only conventions without any valid basis; it is possible that from the long acceptance of this typification we have come to expect men in real life to conform to these conventional types. When the conformity occurs, as it often must, our attention is attracted and our belief is satisfied; and it is possible that when exceptions occur, they are simply passed over and ignored. Many popular beliefs have no basis other than the human peculiarity of seeing only what one wishes to believe or what one has been told to see. The exceptions to the rule may equal the agreements without shaking the belief. In fact, popular beliefs, so-called, are nearly always erroneous; and the more firmly they are held the more surely are they wrong. The human mind when unrestrained by scientific training has to a high degree a faculty for crystallizing fallacies into axioms.

What, then, have those who have made a scientific study of the relation between physique and personality to say on the subject? No final or even positive word has come from them. They have, however, demonstrated striking facts which tend to show a certain degree of relationship. With these facts come many warnings against the dangers of drawing sweeping and unwarranted conclusions. Yet even the little that is known is so useful in making a rough appraisal of certain general traits of personality that we here present it in some detail.

Modern studies of the relation between physique and personality take us at once into the field of the definitely abnormal, the pathological. Much knowledge concerning the workings of the normal brain has been derived from investigations made upon diseased brains, so also information concerning the normal personality has been gathered from the study of the abnormal personality. An analysis of the abnormal personality reveals in exaggerated form the qualities which are to be found in the normal personality. In later chapters, therefore, although our concern is mainly with reasonably normal people, our illustrations will be drawn from the cases of men and women who have definitely psychopathic personalities.

The study of the abnormal to obtain knowledge of the normal is not limited to the field of psychiatry. It applies likewise to physiology. Much of the information concerning the normal functions of the organs of the body—the liver, the kidneys, the stomach—has been obtained from a study of disease states. More information about the peculiarities of the digestive tract is derived from one stomach ache than from any number of meals digested in comfort. And the first serious attempts to correlate physique with personal peculiarities were not made with reference to mental qualities but to susceptibility to certain physical disorders.

Twenty-three hundred years ago the Greek physician Hippocrates defined two types of physique. In the Latin they are termed, respectively, the *habitus apoplepticus* and the *habitus phthysicus*—the physique predisposed to apoplexy and the physique predisposed to consumption. Men of the apoplectic type, those whom Hippocrates believed prone to die of brain hemorrhage, were short and stocky; their chests thick; abdomens full. They had short arms and legs, short, thick necks, round heads and fat faces—the modern John Bull type. Men of the consumptive physique were long and thin; flat chests, long arms and legs, long, slender necks, narrow heads and oval faces—more like the Uncle Sam type.

Even now, after all the centuries that have passed since the days of Hippocrates, scientific investigation has not by any means completely settled the question concerning the relation of physique and predisposition to physical disease. It has confirmed the view that there is a relation, and it has added to the list of diseases. Short and stocky men are more susceptible, it would seem, to diseases of the blood vessels (as Hippocrates noted) and to gall stones and pernicious anæmia than are tall, thin men, among whom, in turn, there seems to be a higher prevalence of tuberculosis as well as an especial tendency toward disturbances of digestion and chronic infections.

The relation between physique and disease, although it lends itself to investigation far more readily than the relation between physique and personality, is, nevertheless, an extremely involved matter, as may be seen in regard to tuberculosis. Hippocrates believed that consumption was the result of a breaking down or wearing out of the body. According to his views, thin men had less durability than fat men, who in turn lost their advantage because of their unfortunate tendency to explode blood vessels. Since the time of Hippocrates the simplicity of this concept has been destroyed by the knowledge that consumption is not a general disintegration of the body, but is a disease caused by a specific bacillus, the tubercle bacillus, which is spread from those who have the disease. Tuberculosis, as an infection, is acquired alike by the fat and the thin, the deep-chested and the flat-chested. It would not occur at all if the spread of the bacteria were stopped. Fat men, however, appear definitely more resistant to the growth of tubercle bacilli within their bodies than do thin men. But, and here is the second complicating factor, no field of medicine is more beset with technical difficulties of research and more surrounded with an atmosphere of popular misconception than that of resistance to infection. It is a proven fact, however, that the progress of this particular infection—tuberculosis—is influenced by general health and vigor: the robust succumb less readily to the disease than do the weak. Perhaps the *habitus phthysicus* of Hippocrates signifies merely that a greater number of robust men are to be found among those who are short, stocky, and tend to be fat, than among those who are tall and slender.

It is with this same cautious attitude against making too direct and sweeping inferences that we now approach the question of the relationship between physique and personality.

The basis for the knowledge of a valid relationship

between physique and personality has its origin in observations made upon the insane. Parenthetically, let us say that this word "insane," which we have used here only for clarity, carries with it archaic connotations that maintain absurd prejudices toward those who suffer from mental diseases. We shall hereafter refer to them, in the hope that others may follow the example, as the mentally ill.

The observations concerning physique and personality from which our digression carried us were to this effect: the great majority of the mentally ill fall into one or another of two groups. One is called the manic-depressive, and the other, the schizophrenic. The differentiation is made according to the mental symptoms exhibited by the patients; and these will be described shortly. The important fact here is this: those who suffer from the manic-depressive condition are mainly of a stocky physique resembling the *habitus apoplepticus* of Hippocrates. Among those suffering from schizophrenia there is rarely found a man of this physique. Instead, the majority are of the slender form, the ancient *habitus phthysicus*.

Among the schizophrenics are found also a considerable number whose physiques approximate neither of these two classifications. There is, however, in this intermediate group, sufficient uniformity in types of physique to afford a basis for further classification, and so the terms athletic and dysplastic have come into use. Moreover, in the general reclassification which has resulted, the terms *apoplepticus* and *phthysicus* have been dropped as unsuited to matters of psychiatry and replaced by the terms pyknic and leptosome. *Pyknic* means fat; *leptosome* means thin-bodied. These terms

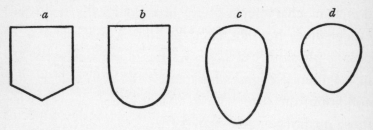

a. flat five-cornered. *b.* broad shield-shape. *c.* long egg-shape. *d.* short egg-shape.

Facial Types as defined by Kretchmer

incidentally illustrate a rather chaotic state in medical etymology. Pyknisome would correspond to leptosome, but pyknic and leptosome it is, and so it will undoubtedly remain, niceties of the language to the contrary.

From the physique of an individual a reasonably accurate estimate can be made of the symptoms he would show if he were to become mentally ill. But the prediction, interesting as it may be to the psychiatrist in making a diagnosis, affords no assistance in evaluating the personality of the "normal" man unless there exists some connection between the nature of the personality and the tendency to a particular form of mental disease. Such a connection appears to exist.

The general character of the symptoms that a man exhibits during mental illness corresponds to the natural tendencies that characterize his personality. His behavior is a caricaturization of his normal qualities; his predominant characteristics are brought to the front and exaggerated, but not altered. Thus a man who is of pyknic physique has those qualities of personality which in heightened degree characterize the manic-depressive condition; the man who is of leptosomic physique has those qualities which characterize schizophrenia.

Patients with the manic-depressive form of mental illness do not all behave precisely alike; neither do those with the schizophrenic form. But each form of illness is typified by an outstanding peculiarity, an attitude toward the realities of life. The man suffering from the manic-depressive condition never loses his hold on material realities; he does not cut himself off from the world; he is social and not asocial. Even at the heights of his mania and in the depths of his depression he is an intense realist, although a grotesque one. On the contrary, the man with the schizophrenic illness loses his hold on realities and his social feelings for the group. He cuts himself off from the world and lives in a bizarre universe created in his own imagination. These two extreme conditions caricature the realist and the idealist, the social and asocial individuals in everyday life.

The significance of these qualities will become more apparent later in this chapter, with further discussion of these two forms of mental illnesses and the corresponding qualities of personality. We turn here to a more detailed description of the physical qualities that give visible clues to the realistic and the idealistic tendencies inherent in the separate personalities. The differentiation of physical types, as will be seen, is more involved than the mere separation of fat men from lean ones.

The fat deposit from which the pyknic physique derives its name does not, as a rule, make its appearance until the approach of middle life. Nor is the pyknic merely a fat man; many fat people belong to the dysplastic rather than the pyknic group. The true pyknic is characterized by the roundness of all parts of his body and the great volume of the cavities, the chest, abdomen, and skull. The thick-set trunk of the pyknic appears almost barrel-shaped. The neck affords a particularly distinguishing feature; it is short and thick, often so short that the chin seems to emerge from the top of the chest. The shoulders do not appear broad or prominent; the fact that the deep chest widens out toward its lower part makes the shoulders seem narrower than they really are. The head of the pyknic is usually round and frequently the hair is lost in middle age, leaving it smoothly bald—not the patchy baldness of the leptosome. The face is full and has in front view the general outline of a pentagon, or shield. The fat of the pyknic is a smooth and even deposit, particularly about the trunk. The outlines of the muscles in the legs and arms are obliterated, but the limbs are not disfigured. The skin is firm, neither loose and flabby, as in the leptosome, nor tightly bound down as in the athletic type.

The pyknic physique in the full display of its richest peculiarities as reached in late middle age is typified in Mr. Pickwick or Jack Falstaff. On the other hand, literature affords no better example of the leptosome than Don Quixote.

The leptosome is characterized by the lack of volume in the cavities of his body. He gives the impression of being taller than he really is. The chest is long and flat and does not widen out toward the lower part. The legs and arms are long and thin, with lean muscles. The face is egg-shaped and in profile usually angular and irregular, with a long nose, and a pointed or receding chin. The head is frequently long and narrow. The neck, again a characterizing feature, is long and equally thin. In middle life the leptosome may acquire some fat, but the deposits do not change his general characteristics.

Pure leptosome and pyknic physiques represent the extremes of two definite and complete types of body form. The qualities of each are transmitted by heredity. The ancestry of some individuals is such that they inherit nearly the pure physique of one type or the other. But among the forebears of most individuals—the average men—there are both pyknics and leptosomes. This mixed ancestry results in a physique in which the features of both of the pure types are present in some degree. The preponderance of the one or the other correspondingly marks the man as being nearer to the pyknic or to the leptosome group both in physique and in personality.

A third physique appears as the *athletic*. The mental traits associated with it are the same as those of the leptosome group. In spite of the fact that the term athletic is applied to a type of physique, it does not follow that those who have it are athletes. The dis-

A Face of the "Long Egg-Shape".
From a drawing made in "Bedlam" London, 1838

tinguishing characteristic of this physique is the heavy development of the bones and especially of the muscles, which stand out in sharp relief. The shoulders are wide in comparison with the hips; the chest is well developed; the abdomen is small; the trunk tapers toward the lower part. The neck is long, but differs from that of the leptosome in that the shoulder muscles rise far up the sides. The face is usually of the long egg-shape. In its full development this physique approaches the ideal of classic masculine beauty as depicted by sculptors. It is the delight of any tailor, for on such a frame the coat hangs straight and unwrinkled from the shoulders and the crease of the trousers follows a straight line over the shapely thighs. These sartorial advantages are not shared by the pyknic: his clothes wrinkle with every move of his bulging body.

An athletic physique, as we have said, does not of itself signify athletic prowess. In fact, many frail men have this physique. Common observation reveals the wide variety of physiques among athletes. Shot-putters, weight-lifters, and wrestlers are predominantly of the pyknic physique, although some wrestlers are distinctly dysplastic. Among the distance runners the leptosome is most in evidence. The athletic physique, when the muscles are powerful as well as prominent, is perhaps best typified in the crew man.

The final group, the dysplastic, are, as the name implies, the unsymmetrically built. To it belong those who show a stunted or abnormal growth of parts of the body: men with long, slender legs, broad, feminine hips, and scanty growth of hair on the body, but a good growth on the scalp; and women with conspicuously masculine figure and features. Other dysplastics are abnormally fat, those especially in whom the deposit is flabby or unsymmetrical: the individual who has enormous thighs and a slender torso or a round, fat abdomen and "spidery" arms and legs. Again, the dysplastic may appear physically underdeveloped: the individual who shows infantile features, with nose too small for the face —sometimes considered "cute" in girls, but hardly so in men. The dysplastic group includes all those whose bodies give the impression of a grotesque combination of poorly matched parts rather than one of consistent physique with harmony of features.

Practice in observation soon leads to proficiency in distinguishing the various physiques. The rotogravure section of the newspaper is a prolific field for types, and they can be studied there without giving offense. The shield-shaped face and rotund figure of the pyknic will be found among the leaders in political events and among the front-row spectators at athletic contests and the theater. The typical short egg-shaped faces, the "perfect ovals," of the leptosomes peer out from the page of debutantes, with only here and there a pyknic face to relieve the uniformity. The sections devoted to male fashions and cinema actors show a predominance of the athletic physique. For the dysplastic one must usually, but by no means always, turn to the unposed pictures.

There is not only a pleasure in identifying the type, but there is also a wealth of information imparted when one can say, "this man is a typical pyknic," or "that one a leptosome" or "so and so" has an athletic or dysplastic physique. It is more than mere physical build that is being designated; a trait of personality is being indicated as well.

And when behavior is watched as well as physique the conviction will come that in this world of hard realities blessed is he with the joys of life who has the pyknic physique. But there are also some disadvantages in this physique—disadvantages other than in the obvious one of wrinkled garments. The main one is an inherent tendency to sudden changes of mood. These mood-swings, far more prevalent among those with this pyknic physique than those with the leptosomic, will be discussed at length in the chapter on temperament. But briefly, they resemble the change from excitement to depression which characterizes the manic-depressive illness. Without apparent cause the mood alters from cheerfulness to gloominess; from optimism to pessimism; and then reverts again to the cheerfulness or optimism. Sometimes there are spells merely of exhilaration without the corresponding depression, or fits of depression without the exhilaration. Frequently the change of mood is slight, but occasionally it is extreme, developing almost to the point of incapacitating "blueness."

These mood-swings are often severely trying to the individual afflicted; they are equally trying to those about him; they are generally misunderstood by both. Much, however, can be done to control them or to discount their effects when the individual learns, and his friends learn also, that the cause lies within the man and not in the world about him. Change of mood is characteristic of his personality and is to be expected. But when the insight is lacking, the man—and this applies to moody women as well—almost invariably puts the blame for the reaction on something outside of himself, on others. To him nothing is more irritating than the solicitation of his friends, carrying with it, as

A Face of the "Short Egg-Shape".
From a drawing made in "Bedlam" London, 1838

it must, the imputation that something is wrong with him; and accompanied, as it always is, by the well-meant queries, "Why are you gloomy? What's the matter?" Often it requires experience gained from many unpleasant episodes before his associates learn to refrain from asking, "What's the matter?" and simply await the inevitable return of a more pleasant mood.

In spite of this tendency to mood-swings, the qualities inherent in the personality associated with the pyknic physique make for a fuller appreciation of the good things of life than do those associated with the leptosomic physique. The bodily activities of the pyknic appear to function more harmoniously than do those of the leptosome. For this reason, if no other, it is a regrettable fact that at present the pyknic physique is outmoded. In a highly civilized community the ideals of sex attraction are invariably set by vogues. For no obvious cause, the fashion for sex attraction in physique now favors the leptosome and the athletic physiques rather than the pyknic. At the moment the slender form is fashionable for women and "nobody loves a fat man." Physique is hereditary; the regrettable dictum of fashion is now to breed for leptosomes. And one may well speculate on the ultimate social outcome of the tendency if it persists.

Indeed, far too little attention has been paid to the influence of fashion on sexual selection in shaping national characteristics. Feminine fashion has more than once aped the coloring and posture of definite disease states, placing a premium on the abnormal. But fashions have a way of changing: the "sun-tan" complexion replaced the "consumptive make-up"; bustles and padded bosoms may again return to reflect a preference for the pyknic physique. Fortunately, the full display of the pyknic characteristics often lies partially dormant until after the age of marriage. Slender, but shapely young ladies expand amazingly into portly matrons of the "motherly" type. The true leptosomic female, however, retains always the "old maid's physique" and true old maids, be it said parenthetically, are born so both in physique and personality. They remain "old maids" even in marriage.

This digression on moods and marriage has carried us far beyond the intention of this chapter. We return to a description of the symptoms of mental illness. First, the manic-depressive condition which, as we have reiterated, is that illness which reveals the peculiar personality traits of individuals of the pyknic physique. Manic-depressive is a rather recent term; it replaces the names formerly given to two supposedly different conditions, mania and melancholy, now known to be separate phases of one form of mental illness. The man with mania—the maniac of the past—exhibits great excitement; his mood is one of exhilaration. He moves incessantly, shouting, talking, laughing. Occasionally, when his demands are ignored, he bursts into violent rage, tearing at the furniture of his room and attacking his attendants. The most trivial matters occupy his attention; he moves from object to object as they catch his eye; he is distracted by everything, persists in nothing. Usually he is keen of wit and quick; too quick, often, for observers to follow his discursive sallies. He is a man of mood and action. When unmolested, the joy of living, of moving, of being in contact with the things about him, fills him to overflowing.

The man with so-called melancholy is entirely different. His are the deepest gloom and the slowest action. The sorrow of living grieves him almost unbearably. He sits motionless, brooding, his face drawn in an expression of pain. He does not attack his attendants; he ignores them. Their taunts can add nothing to the feeling of sorrow that racks him. But he must be watched constantly, for there comes a time when he moves more freely; he appears less depressed; an agitation, a sense of tension, of apprehension, fills him. Then perhaps he will attempt to end his grief in suicide. Escaping this end, he, like the man with mania, usually recovers from his attack of mental illness—perhaps never to suffer from it again.

Mania and melancholy appear totally unlike, but modern psychiatry has shown them to be the same disease. The melancholy is merely the reverse of the mania. One is the phase of stimulation; the other the phase of depression. With some men the symptoms of the disease appear only in the depressive phase; with others, only in the exhilarated phase. There are still others in whom both phases are present, one alternating with the other in cycles. Such an individual passes from the peak of exhilaration and vivacity to the depths of grief and immobility.

The manic-depressive condition is by no means always as severe as we have described it. There are often border-line cases ranging in all degrees between the "normal" man who merely vacillates in mood and action to the one who shows true illness. In many of these intermediate stages the peculiarity of behavior is permanent; it is often sufficiently marked to deserve the name of hypomanic—less than manic. A hypomanic is not quite normal; neither is he definitely ill. Hypomanics are found in all walks of life. Certainly every

A Face of the General Pyknic Type.
From a drawing made in "Bedlam" London, 1838

reader numbers among his acquaintances at least one who shows in some degree the traits of the hypomanic described here:

"He rises full of schemes of business or pleasure. He fusses noisily about the house, indifferent to his disturbance of other people's slumbers. He is very impatient of delay, he cannot wait a minute for anything he wants. The course of the post is not expeditious enough for him. He sends his letters by telegraph, and his letters are extraordinarily numerous. They would be numerous in any case, but their number is doubled, and more than doubled, by the frequent changes of his mind and by the impulsiveness with which he acts upon every passing whim. He determines to make some purchase, probably a very unnecessary one, but one for which he can adduce twenty plausible reasons, and he writes to tell his solicitor that he will call the next morning. Scarcely is the letter posted when he sees that he will attain his object more quickly by asking his solicitor to lunch. He telegraphs accordingly. Before his messenger returns, it occurs to him that he had better ask the vendor to lunch also. Another telegram is dispatched, and since he cannot entertain more than one visitor at his club, another must be sent to the solicitor to announce the change to a hotel. Then he remembers that he has been drawing heavily of late on his bank account, and that he may not have the necessary funds available. Another telegram to the bank. But if there are insufficient funds in the bank, he will have to sell stock to raise the funds; another telegram to his broker. Then he determines that it will be better to pledge the stock at the bank rather than sell it. More telegrams to the broker and to the bank. The broker won't like the contradictory orders—never mind; ask him to dinner—ask them all to dinner. Put off the lunch and have a dinner instead and ask the solicitor, the vendor, the banker, and the broker. Yes, and why not Smith and Jones and Robinson as well? More telegrams; and then, since two out of three of the invited guests decline, the whole thing is postponed, also by telegraph. Meantime, in the intervals of telegraphing, his hands have been full. He has been constantly ringing the bell and giving orders—giving them, modifying them, and countermanding them—constantly wanting something fresh, running up and down the stairs, writing letters, haranguing this person and that . . . and talking almost incessantly."[1]

In short, the hypomanic is a human dynamo; he is the high-pressure salesman; the expansive, aggressive,

[1] Mercer, Charles, *A Text Book of Insanity*. London, 1902.

insistent member of the board of directors who, unless he is held back by his more normal associates, will ruin his company with expansion and change. Such hypomanics, when highly intelligent, are often very productive men. They reach high positions in the commercial and industrial world, particularly when they have assistants who are not merely "yes men," but men who will brave the tempest to veto wild ideas and carry valid ones through to completion. Hypomanics seem indefatigable, but many have occasional periods of depression which they sometimes hide with the name of a "nervous breakdown." They take their "rest" in a sanitarium. Their friends then exclaim: "No wonder! No man can carry on at such a pace; he has overworked!" The business associates, and subordinates, and wife and children as well, obtain a much needed rest during his absence.

The manic-depressive, the hypomanic, the man with mood-swings, are all realists in their outlook upon the world. Their behavior is always conceived in terms of reality, usually a social reality. In a mood of exhilaration they cannot enjoy their pleasures alone; they must talk, and see, and feel, and hear everything about them. In a mood of depression they are still in contact with realities, but the joy of participation is gone. Men and things oppress them. They may attempt to escape by the realistic method of self-annihilation; but they never try to evade things as they are by creating a more pleasant world of imaginative unreality. Their personalities are rooted in the fact of social and human relationships and such their world must always remain.

Unlike the manic-depressive, the man suffering from schizophrenia withdraws from reality and lives in a world of his own creation, influenced neither by the men nor by the events about him. In its last stages this disease destroys the final bond between the mind and the external world. This stage was the only one noted by early medical observers who called the disease dementia. Later, it was believed to occur only in the young, and so it was termed dementia præcox. But now with greater knowledge of the symptoms the term no longer fits; the disease does not always lead to dementia nor does it occur only in the young. The one feature that it does show invariably in all of its many forms is withdrawal from the realities of life—a splitting of the psyche, schizophrenia.

Schizophrenia is not a disease of mood or motion, an exaggeration of joy or depression, like the manic-depressive illness. The schizophrenic appears instead to draw a screen between himself and the world of re-

A Face of the Extreme Pyknic Type—"Broad Shield-Shape".

ality. Behind this screen he elaborates a world of fantasy. The actual symptoms of the disease appear in many different forms, depending in part upon the extent of the patient's self-seclusion. Thus in some forms the schizophrenic is secretive, suspicious of those about him, withdrawing from them, indifferent to his daily tasks, his home ties, and his social relations; he is callous in his personal obligations and to the feelings of others.

In other forms of the disease the patient shuts himself off more completely from realities. He lives a life apart, as strange to normal men as if he were from another world. Only vaguely can we glimpse his meanings from his muttered words and gather here and there a reflection of the fantastic universe in which he lives. His actions become as unreal as his words; they are bizarre and non-human. For days he lies in a stupor, refuses to eat or drink or talk, and would even die if he were not fed with a tube; again he assumes a rigid pose and holds it tirelessly for weeks; or again day in and day out in monotonous repetition he makes motions back and forth—rubs his head, rocks his chair, staring intently. Sometimes the patient lapses into dementia from which we have no glimmering of his thoughts and fantasies. He lives in the world, but not of it.

The manifestations of schizophrenia show in greatly exaggerated form a propensity common to many people —particularly those of leptosome, athletic, and dysplastic physiques. It is the tendency to build fantasies as a substitute for the realities of life. Now nearly everyone can enjoy moments of fantasy; the child's make-believe is fantasy and so also is the daydreaming of the adolescent boy; the novel and the theater are worlds of unrealities in which most people find pleasure and real living. But from the unrealities some men can move aside the screen entirely and see life clearly, meet men, like them, respond to their moods and wishes, and interpret realities as realities. Such is the reaction which we usually associate with men of the pyknic physique. Others do not so easily relinquish their dream world; they live in its shadow, finding their pleasures away from men. They are shut in; their joys come from the unrealities: from the technicalities of theology; the exactitudes of logic; the intricacies of invention; the speculation of metaphysics; the idealism of reform; the symbolism and romance of poetry; or, on a lower plane, from the exercise of the crossword puzzle and the stamp collection; from the seclusion of the workshop hobby, or the novel, the movies, or just plain daydreaming.

It is, as we have stated repeatedly, with due reservations, that we deal with the correlation between physique and personality. The scientific study of the subject is still in its infancy. The physique component of personality affords at most merely glimpses of certain qualities, of certain tendencies of the personality. And yet in many cases these tendencies must shape the choice of a course in life. We should expect to find men of pyknic physique by their preference in occupations dealing with men; they are at their best as the salesman, the trial lawyer, the practicing physician, the politician —social occupations. The leptosome would find his place one of equal importance, but more in the background of active affairs, as the planner, the schemer, the organizer, the theorist, the inventor, and the research worker. In successful careers we see some exceptions to such a rule, for at best it is not dogmatic. And, since all men do not choose the paths in life for which their traits best suit them, we see also many obvious misfits and many failures.

The German psychiatrist, Dr. E. Kretchmer, a leader in the modern studies of the relation of physique to personality, has summarized the tendencies associated with the types of physique. His table, slightly modified, is given here.

	Pyknic physique (social tendencies)	*Leptosome physique* (asocial tendencies)
Poets	Realists Humorists	Pathetics Romantics Formalists
Experimenters	Observers Describers Empiricists	Exact logicians Systematists Metaphysicians
Leaders	Jolly organizers Understanding conciliators	Pure idealists Despots and fanatics Cold calculators

Observation of men in public life will show that in the great majority of cases the correlation between physique and the natural tendencies of the personality is borne out. There are, of course, some definite exceptions. There are also many instances when neither the physique nor the tendencies are clear-cut examples of the extremes defined here; both fall into an intermediate class. Thus Abraham Lincoln exhibited both practical and idealistic qualities, and mood-swings as well; his physique was predominantly leptosomic and athletic. Ulysses S. Grant, the practical handler of men, was, however, of definite pyknic physique. John Locke was a striking example of the leptosome physique; Benjamin Franklin typified equally the pyknic. Both were philosophers. But Locke was a rigid formalist, a metaphysician; while Franklin was primarily a practical man of affairs, and only secondarily a utilitarian philosopher. It is almost impossible to find a striking pyknic physique among the group of men who have achieved fame as philosophers.

Calvin was a leptosome and had in a high degree the peculiar tendencies of personality associated with that physique. He was a cold, technical theologian. Mirabeau, on the contrary, was of pyknic physique; he had the tendencies associated with that physique; he became the "people's man," a popular leader. Because of the same circumstances of hereditary endowment Theodore Roosevelt and Grover Cleveland had the ability to command practical affairs and deal with realities.

But none of these men, or any other men, were preordained by the tendencies of his personality to the actual rôle he filled in life. The tendencies associated with their physiques fitted them to fill a multitude of positions: both Locke and Calvin might have spent their lives as bookkeepers, as village schoolmasters, as drafters of legal briefs, as bibliophiles, as sentimental or symbolic poets, as political theorists, as cubist artists. But neither of them could have been practical handlers of men; neither could have filled successfully the position of gang foreman in a lumber camp; or bartender; or drill sergeant; or trial lawyer playing on a jury; or practical philosopher such as Benjamin Franklin; or family physician. But such positions among others might have been open to Mirabeau and Cleveland and Roosevelt.

Some of the greatest tragedies in public life have occurred when a true leptosome with his accompanying tendencies has tried to play the part of a practical realist. Robespierre was such. A dry schoolmaster and technical jurist, a follower of Rousseau's idealistic principles of government, he attempted to translate his ideals into action. He succeeded only in becoming a cold-blooded, but virtuous murderer. Woodrow Wilson presents another instance of the idealist frustrated by the practicalities of political affairs. Honoré Mirabeau, or Grover Cleveland, or Theodore Roosevelt, or Benjamin Franklin would have been equally frustrated if they had had forced upon them the rôles of technical theologians or symbolic poets.

Nor do we need seek in such elevated walks of life for our examples of the misfits. The typical leptosomic "grind" in college trying to be a good fellow, a cheer leader, usually succeeds only in making an ass of himself. Equally pathetic, but far more tragic, is the boy of pyknic physique who is forced by his family to take courses in humanistic subjects which do not appeal to him. He may struggle through, but when independence comes, he will usually strike out for a field of endeavor suited to his tendencies. Or he may also remain a misfit. The leptosome entering politics on a reform ticket— that is his usual entry—is soon submerged by the practical politicians who are almost invariably of pyknic physique.

These tendencies of personality associated with physique are displayed not only in occupation, but in every phase of activity; they express the nature of the man's relation to his entire environment. Some men are born to do best in one kind of environment; some to do best in another. Calvin and Mirabeau, exposed to environments different from those they encountered, would have led different lives. But no force from the environment would have changed the fundamental nature of their personalities; in all environments they would have maintained the identity of their personalities even as they would have maintained the identity of their physiques. No environment could ever have made a Calvin of Mirabeau, or a Mirabeau of Calvin. But for the grace of his particular environment, Woodrow Wilson might have been a Calvin, but there is no environment which could have shaped him into a Theodore Roosevelt, an Honoré Mirabeau, a Grover Cleveland, or a Benjamin Franklin.

MIRABEAU.

PART III

FREEDOM THAT GROWS WITH THE MIND

Chapter III

FREEDOM THAT GROWS WITH THE MIND

═══════════════════════════════════════

THE clues to the structure of the human body and of the human personality lie in evolution—a simultaneous biological evolution.

The development of a child before birth is an epitome of evolution. There in the womb of every mother each child recapitulates in the course of a few weeks the stages of development that have taken place during eons of evolution—from the one-celled organism to man. In rapid kaleidoscopic change the great steps are reënacted. For a moment the one-celled organism appears, the human egg. Then in minutes and hours, instead of the thousands of centuries of evolution, it becomes a multi-cellular organism, the human embryo. But it is an embryo with gill slits in its neck duplicating momentarily that stage of evolution where the highest forms of animal life were still aquatic. Then lungs develop and the gill slits close over, leaving mere remnants; life has passed from the aquatic to the amphibian and terrestrial forms. Then the brain bulges, the head expands, and finally the unmistakable human form emerges.

Such matters are not mere fanciful speculation or imagery. They are soundly proven biological facts. They are visible, tangible.

In the passage of these same weeks in which the flesh is shaped to its predestined form, the personality is laid together element by element. And these elements find their places in precisely the same order, in precisely the same structure, in which they have appeared in all animals during evolution.

Impulse was the first element of personality. It is the ancient evolutionary foundation upon which all personality is built. Next in order of appearance was temperament. And finally there were developed those elements which are less stable and vastly more complex than the older ones and which we call ego and intelligence.

All animals from the very lowest to the very highest possess an impulse-life. An impulse is a basic biological need for which a satisfaction is sought. The sources of satisfaction lie outside the body. Without impulse-life animals would perish; none can exist wholly on itself.

Impulse-life achieved its full development early in evolution. It was established before a rudimentary brain, before even a nervous system developed. The impulses for food and sex and self-protection are not of the brain, but of the flesh and fiber of the body.

In the lowest form of life impulse alone satisfies all the requirements of an elementary personality; there is no temperament, no ego, no intelligence, merely impulse directly in contact with the environment. Later acquisitions, which give the human personality its complexity, do not change the nature of the basic impulses; they merely allow a greater scope and variety to the sources from which satisfaction is achieved. The impulse for food that causes the one-celled amœba of ditch water to engulf a solid particle, that drives the frog to snap at a fly, the tiger to rend an antelope, and the man to eat his meals, differs no particle among the four. The impulse itself is the undifferentiated urge for food, for the satisfaction of a basic biological need, irrespective of the character of the behavior by which the need is satisfied. The spider that devours her conjugal consort, the salmon that swims to its spawning-ground to die, and the young couple who price houses in the suburbs are actuated by identical impulses—the basic biological urge of sex.

The element of personality called temperament appears higher in the scale of evolutionary development than does impulse, for the presence of temperament necessitates at least the rudiments of a brain, an integrating center for the emotional life. The amœba and the oyster have no emotional life. Insects, however, do have emotions; they have temperament. But theirs is group temperament rather than individual; all the members of a species react alike as definitely as they appear alike. Mosquitoes and wasps have distinctly different temperaments, but all mosquitoes of the same breed have the same temperament and all wasps of the same breed have the same temperament. There are varieties of bees that for bees are gentle and easy to handle; there are others that are irritable and fiery; the apiarists can at a glance predict the emotional peculiarities of bees from their shape and size and coloring—their variety. And mosquitoes and wasps can be similarly classified.

Still higher in the evolutionary scale individuality of temperament is superimposed upon group temperament. This fact is strikingly evident in domestic animals. All dogs possess a basic canine temperament that is different from those of cows or cats or chickens. And in addition each of the kinds of dogs exhibit peculiarities of temperament that are characteristic of the variety, such as differentiate the warm but ponderous phlegmatism of the Saint Bernard from the snappy vivacity of the Pomeranian. And finally, each separate dog of each separate breed exhibits peculiarities of temperament that characterizes it as an individual.

This same individuality exists among human beings and probably in not much greater degree of variation than among brute animals on the level of the dog. As in the case of impulse, man has not evolved appreciably above other animals in temperament. His emotions and moods are those also of the brute animals; with them he shares anxiety, depression, cheerfulness, gloom, vivacity, phlegmatism, warmth, and coldness.

The fact that temperament appeared early in evolutionary development suggests that this element of personality is centered in a lower part of the brain—one of the first wings, so to speak, added to the basic foundations of the nervous system. And such, in fact, is the case. Temperament is controlled by the thalamus, a mass of nerve cells near the base of the brain just above the portion that regulates such deeply-seated functions as respiration and circulation. The thalamus is also concerned with the functions of sight and hearing. When in the evolutionary process eyes and ears developed and the outside world was seen and heard, temperament also developed.

The addition of temperament to the more basic quality of impulse brings in the first stage of complexity to the personality. No longer is impulse-life in direct contact with the environment. The impulse in going outward becomes surrounded by and imbued with emotional qualities. Likewise the impulse can no longer be reached directly from the outside; the force exerted upon it can reach it only after it has been acted upon by temperament; only after it has been selected by the emotional qualities and colored by them. Hunger rises at the sight of food; the sex impulse can be excited in man by a touch. But the food that arouses delight in one man may cause disgust in another; the kiss that brings forth a burst of passion in one is revolting to another.

Human personality rises both in an evolutionary and in a real superiority over that of all other animals. The bulging forepart of man's brain and skull is his emblem of superiority. Intelligence has its seat in the last evolutionary acquisition of the brain, a portion of the cortex or outer surface of the cerebrum. Deprived of the use of this portion of the brain a man would still live, but in his behavior he would appear to have dropped far downward in the scale of evolution. He would retain all his impulses; he would have desires. He would show his emotions, for he would still have his temperament. But he would have lost all restraint. He could not develop a character; he could not become civilized or cultured. He would be and would remain a human brute.

Due to developmental defects, children of this mental state are occasionally born; they are the lowest grade of idiots. Because of some brain diseases, men are sometimes deprived of intelligence. They become demented. They have wants; they have rages and pleasures of a kind; but they must be cared for in institutions.

In acquiring intelligence man has become far more dependent upon this component of personality than are any of the lower animals. They, lacking his degree of intelligence, are endowed with highly developed instincts. Most of man's instincts have been overlaid by highly adaptable qualities afforded by intelligence.

In using the word instinct we pause to define it in the sense in which we employ it here. There are many different connotations of the word; indeed, judging from its uses, many different definitions. Instinct is not impulse. Instinct is not a biological urge. Instead it is an inborn mode of behavior by which the impulse is guided to its goal for satisfaction. The sexual instinct is not the urge for satisfaction; it is the way in which the urge is satisfied. It is instinct that guides the queen bee and the drone in their nuptial flight and the salmon in its long swim to the spawning-ground, but in both cases and in both animals the impulse is precisely the same. The instinct, and the mode of behavior, are different. An instinct cannot be aroused; only the impulse can be aroused. Instinct is, so to speak, inborn character. It is a definite and unyielding mode of behavior dictated by the very structure of the nervous system.

Such stereotyped behavior makes no allowance for individuality; correspondingly, it does away with all need for thought or decision. When, in an animal guided only by instinct, the impulse of hunger, or sex, or self-preservation is aroused, that animal and all of its kind behave in one definite manner. The sexual habits of the bee and the salmon are monotonous in their precise and predictable uniformity. A drone bee that courted the queen in any other way than with the fatal flight would, in slang, "be news." The oyster that at a certain age attaches itself to a rock, opens its shell to obtain food, closes it again when its shell is touched, surrounds an irritating grain of sand with pearl—in short performs the entire range of activities that an oyster is capable of performing, requires no education or training to do these things. The complete "character" of the oyster is built into the structure of its rudimentary nervous system. As a result it can act in no other way.

Higher in the scale of animal development the instincts persist and in some cases, as in ants and bees, are elaborated to control enormously complicated systems of behavior. The elaborate social system, in fact the whole mode of living, of these insects is automatic; ants and bees do not have individual characters in the sense that mice and men have. They have inborn group characters. The only way their behavior can change is with a change in the structure of the animals themselves. The division of labor among bees—queen, drones, workers—results only from recognizable differences in physical structures which have their effect on the nervous system and hence upon the instincts. Drones are males, queens are true females, and workers sexually undeveloped females. The life behavior for each is determined at the moment the egg is laid.

Birds, still higher in the evolutionary scale, show instinctive reaction to a high degree, but they are also capable of developing personal peculiarities of behavior. Thus a chicken hatched from an egg in an incubator, reared under artificial heat, and never brought into contact with an older bird, will not only develop in a normal manner, but will breed, make its nest, hatch and rear its young in precisely the same manner as do chickens hatched under a hen and reared with parental care. In carrying out these fundamental acts, even though an elaborate system of behavior must be enacted, the bird does not require instruction; it needs no character formation in selecting the goal for its impulses or shaping the modes by which these goals are reached.

Chickens, indeed all birds, in spite of the fact that they are controlled basically by instincts, have sufficient intelligence to permit some small degree of character formation—of individuality of behavior. They can be domesticated; they can be made into pets; they can be taught to perform complicated procedures which are not instinctive with them.

Instinct and character have their individual advantages and disadvantages. The particular disadvantages of instinct lie in the rigid limitations it imposes. But with this limitation all social problems are removed; they have been solved for all time. An animal controlled by instinct can only to a very small degree alter its way of living. Such an animal cannot make progress, cannot advance to higher planes of living. But neither can it regress. And there lies the great advantage of instinct. Oysters, bees, and ants have for countless generations lived in precisely the same way they live today;

no doubt they will be living the same way countless generations in the future. Only by a process of evolution accompanied by changes in physical structure will they alter their ways. And then they will cease to be oysters and bees and ants.

The advantage of character formation lies in the flexibility and the adaptability of behavior which it allows. Man can progress, can seek and attain new goals, improve his condition over that of his forebears. He can do so because he is in a large degree emancipated from those instinctive patterns of behavior which would otherwise give him a predetermined mode of action. He has intelligence.

With the emancipation from instincts, with the acquisition of intelligence, there has been given to man not only the opportunity, but also the responsibility of character formation. That opportunity postulates the acquisition of a great diversity of goals for the satisfaction of his impulses and that responsibility requires that these goals be limited, as far as possible, to standards set by fellow men.

The vast difference that exists in the behavior of a crude savage, on the one hand, and that of a civilized and polished gentleman on the other, is largely a matter of character formation. As different as their "manners" appear, only a single lifetime separates the two. "Under the skin" both are actuated by identically the same impulses, but each has set up different goals and values, has acquired different modes of behavior to achieve satisfaction. Who shall say that one is biologically superior to the other; that one obtains more satisfaction and contentment in life than the other? Any answer will inevitably be prejudiced; a man not only sees and judges the world through the temperament and ego and intelligence with which he is endowed, but also through the character that he has acquired.

Wide as are the apparent differences in human manners, there are nevertheless definite limits to their scope. First, behavior is limited by the peculiarities of the general structure of the human personality; a man behaves as a man and not as any other animal; his behavior would always be recognized as that of a human being. And second, it is limited by the special peculiarities of his individual personality; no two men have precisely the same strength of impulse, the same temperament, the same ego, and the same intelligence. Two men placed in the same environment could not develop precisely the same characters. Each would maintain his individuality in spite of all efforts to the contrary. His personality—the individuality of the man—not only predicates his behavior; it also appears in it. Character is the one flexible element in man's total reactions. And character formation is a vastly important aspect of human development.

A baby is born with only a few instinctive patterns of behavior, but with an enormous capacity for character formation. A baby will suck an object placed in its mouth; it will cry, it will grasp an object placed in its hands. Likewise, in time, it will walk without instruction. Still later in life it will show a vague instinctive behavior in regard to sex; instinct, though not clear and diffused, will guide its impulse normally toward the opposite sex. The nervous connections through which these simple instinctive acts are directed are laid down in the anatomical structure of the nervous system. But the baby is not born with the instinctive behavior of what to suck, how to speak, what to grasp in its hand, or where to seek satisfaction for its impulses. Nor is it born with a sense of right or wrong, of justice, of religious beliefs, or of ethical standards—or even of table manners. A baby must learn by experience. This experience is the basis of character formation.

Character is the sum-total of all the relations which the individual establishes with his environment, the sum-total of all the sources of satisfaction and dissatisfaction which have been developed for his impulses.

Day by day, with each new experience, character is formed. With the passage of each day a past is developed for the individual. In every act of the present he reënacts the sum-total of his past. And this past of the individual includes every event, every occurrence, even the most insignificant, that has touched upon his life. As the sum-total of the experience increases in number, each new experience, unless it is overwhelming in its violence, becomes a smaller and smaller percentage of the total. Each, accordingly, has less influence upon the whole. Consequently it is the experiences of childhood that have the most profound influence in forming character. It becomes solid and inflexible with age. In an adult character has become nearly as thoroughly ingrained as has instinct in lower animals. The elderly man no doubt believes that he deliberately chooses each of his paths, that he is a free-thinking, free-acting individual. Nothing is farther from the truth. His decisions all lie in his past.

If in such an individual we were to dissect the complex sexual behavior, or the beliefs on any subject, or the standards of ethics, or any other phase of character, we should see, as the pieces fell before us, that each was a minute fragment of the past. These fragments placed together would build the character of the individual. But if we dissected many characters, we should see also that the fragments derived from any single experience shared by two or more personalities were not precisely alike. The event, with all its surroundings, is experienced by the individual only as it is perceived through *his* individual personality, through *his* intelligence, through *his* ego, through *his* temperament, and, finally, through the strength of *his* impulse. A man of weak impulse, cold temperament, weak ego, and low intelligence derives from an event quite a different experience from that of a man with strong impulse, warm temperament, strong ego, and high intelligence. It is the sensation that each man experiences, not the event itself, that colors, bends, and blends the perception before it acts on character formation. Each individual experiences the environment only as he alone can experience it; his character is built only as his personality alone will allow it to be built in the particular environment in which it is placed. The personality retains its individuality, its identifying features, in any environment.

The similar persistent individuality of physical structure is well recognized. The shape of the body, the color of the hair and eyes, are universally accepted as hereditary qualities. As such they are established for the individual at the moment of conception. The new-born baby is irrevocably predestined by its inheritance to develop—if it survives—a certain general physique and a certain general coloring. Environment does not shape these fundamental qualities. They are independent of climate and of social and economic status and of all desires to the contrary. Even the most extensive training and physical culture cannot change a stocky blond boy into a tall, thin brunette. It may develop in him a multitude of new coördinations; he may learn to play the piano or to play golf, to lay bricks or to set jewels; he may gain a certain posture, a more powerful muscular development, suppleness, and scope of movement; and he may be able to control the amount of fat deposited on his body. But when he has completed all these things—and they are very important things—he will still be a stocky blond individual, and such he will remain.

That these facts, evident in regard to the physical structure, apply also to personality, is not equally recognized. There is still a strong belief—no doubt dictated by the wish of parents, educators, child psychologists, and social reformers—that the personality is wholly plastic and derives its form from environmental influences. One does not have to seek far for the source of this wish: environment can, to some extent, be controlled; heredity, once established, is beyond control. The basic elements of personality are determined by heredity and are therefore established at the moment of conception. Just as in the case of the physique, the baby is irrevocably predestined to develop a certain type of personality by virtue of its genetic component —and nothing can be done about it. Babies are born to be strong or weak in impulse, or some degree between; they are born to be bright or stupid; they are born to be cheerful or gloomy, warm or cold, vivacious or phlegmatic; and they are born to be strong or weak or normal or deviated in ego. And again nothing can be done to alter these peculiarities. The fundamental qualities of personality cannot be altered, but—and here lies a saving grace—their display can be modified by character formation. The weaker and the more deviated the inherent element of personality, the more "good" character formation is needed. And, sad to say, the more difficult it is to achieve. But the fact remains that a man with a deviated personality but highly trained in character may be far more useful and contented than a man with a normal personality but poorly trained in character.

Character cannot be forced upon the personality; it must be adapted to it. Just as it is impossible by physical culture to convert a stocky boy into a tall slender one, or *vice versa*, so also it is impossible by training to convert a phlegmatic child into a vivacious one. It is equally impossible to make a strongly aggressive man out of one who has a weak impulse; to make an optimist out of a pessimist; and to make a bright boy out of a stupid one. Education, training, culture, represent merely controlled and graded experience directed toward the development of character along lines that seem desirable to the educator. Many faults of character formation lie with the educator; most arise from the failure to recognize the fact—or from ignoring it—that inborn personality cannot be altered, that the parent, the educator, the social reformer, must work with the materials that are given to them to work with. When this basic fact has been disregarded, there has come discontent, failure, and revolt for the individual, and disappointment and sorrow for the family. Out of the failures grow new and ever newer schemes of education and of social reform, each in turn to be doomed to its failure unless the limits of individual character formation are taken into consideration.

Character formation by training is as the forging of metal upon an anvil; each blow is an experience; repeated blows finally shape the metal. But there are different metals—lead and iron and brass and silver and gold—and all do not respond the same beneath the hammer. The hammer cannot change the metal, but the metal can and does impose the limits to which it can be shaped. And when the shaping is done the metal shows indelibly in the finished product.

Some personalities have, by the peculiarities of their inborn components, a high degree of malleability, adaptability; others have a very limited adaptability, are rigid and brittle. Some men can adapt their behavior only to simple situations; others to highly complex. The social systems of native peoples are direct and simple; adaptation is correspondingly easy for a wide range of personalities. The social systems in civilization are far more complex, and adaptation far more difficult. Within the civilization itself there are levels of complexity—the isolation of the farm and camp at one extreme and the involved relations and conventions of life in a large city at the other.

The belief that in a civilization a common environment can be shaped to suit all personalities is absurd. With a wide range and choice of environment some personalities find their places in one situation, others in a far different one. Under such a system some men are born to be merchants, some doctors, some lawyers, and some criminals. This statement is not to be taken as a sweeping generalization applying to all men. But for many of those who are deviated in personality no other situations offered in the civilization will suit the display of their peculiarities. Some men enjoy the seclusion and independence of the farm; others flee the farm at an early age and find their satisfaction in some phase of city life; still others flee from the city to the village. Many there are who, by force of circumstances, remain in situations unsuited to their personality—they are the misfits in life. And finally, there are some who can find no satisfaction in any of the normal situations offered by civilization. They may revolt against civilization itself; they may be defeated by it; they may find no escape. A radical alteration of environment, as in the upheaval of war, may form a place for personalities that are misfitted in all peace-time environments. Often fanatical patriots, fiery leaders, even beneficent dictators, are men who have shown no signs of greatness in any ordinary environments—the

Couthons, the Marats, the Robespierres of the French Revolution, and the Mussolinis and the Hitlers of today.

In that rare individual, the so-called "normal" man, all the parts of personality are in well-balanced proportions. The strength of his impulses is compatible with his temperament, and both in turn are compatible with his intelligence and ego. The personality of the normal man is difficult to characterize, as difficult as attempting to characterize the physical structure of a well-built man, a man of average height and weight, of nondescript coloring, possessing no distinguishing peculiarities—unless, indeed, the "normal" is so exceptional as to be in itself a distinguishing feature. And in matters of personality such is virtually the case.

Few personalities indeed exhibit complete harmony of parts; usually one or more of the components exercise, in a small or large degree, a disproportionate influence over the others and so tend to characterize the personality; to color the whole behavior of the man.

Strictly speaking, where such asymmetry of personality exists, no matter how slight it may be, the personality is designated as abnormal and therefore psychopathic. Consequently nearly everyone is psychopathic. But before our reader reacts unfavorably to the suggestion that he may be abnormal, let him pause and ask himself this question: "Am I perfect?" If he finds the answer in the affirmative, let him cease to read further save perhaps for the chapter on the ego. But if he admits the slightest doubt of his own perfection, let him accept the fact that he is psychopathic and read on. And if he does read on, he will no doubt discover this fact in regard to himself as he follows through these pages and finds his own peculiarities described.

The fact that a man has a psychopathic personality does not imply abnormality in all his behavior, or even the necessity of displaying any marked abnormality. If he understands and appreciates his own peculiarities, and if they are not too extreme, he can often control or compensate for them as far as his general behavior is concerned. Such control, however, no matter how successfully accomplished, does not imply that the basic qualities of personality have been altered. Many men who are crippled physically can, by an effort, overcome the handicap of their deformity and become productive individuals. The normal individual, if he made an equally intensive effort, could be even more productive; but often he lacks the incentive. The compensation of the cripple does not alter the existence of the deformity. Neither does it alter the fact that the deformity continues to distinguish the physique of such a man. It is a peculiarity by which he can be classified and identified.

Under the broad definition given here, the term psychopathic does not of necessity imply something unpleasant, or even undesirable. In the realm of physical structure it would be tantamount to saying that few people have absolute perfection of face and figure, have no distinguishing imperfections. In the case of personality the abnormality may be an actual advantage. A disproportionately high degree of intelligence is certainly abnormal, but at times it may be very useful. Cheerfulness and vivacity may be as abnormal as gloom and torpidity; the possession of either group may mark the individual as definitely psychopathic.

It is true also that there are personalities so extremely psychopathic that it is difficult for them to succeed in any situation in life. On the other hand, it is rarely the wholly normal man who is found among those who, by the accepted standards, "succeed in life." Those who are most successful in any field are often strongly marked by some dominating peculiarity of personality that sets them apart from their fellows in the same field and is indeed the mainspring of their success. But the peculiarities in one man which may yield success and power may in another yield nothing more productive than an attack of indigestion or a "nervous breakdown."

When a psychopathic personality is placed in an environment unsuited to its peculiarities—when it is frustrated in attaining its goals—disturbances of personality may occur. The behavior of the individual may then become psychopathic; such is particularly the case if the individual does not understand his own peculiarities, does not have insight into the true cause of his disturbed condition. Psychopathic behavior may take many forms, of which we shall have much more to say later.

A common one is that which is classed as psychoneurosis. The psychoneurotics are those whose disturbances of personality are apt to be carried over into the realm of physical function. They are prone to develop symptoms of physical derangement and physical disease. And the disturbed physical function is, though they would be the first to deny it, of advantage to them in some way, usually as an unconscious evasion of responsibility. The psychoneurotics constitute the great procession of "the lame, the halt, and the blind." And following closely are the multitude whose psychoneurotic tendencies yield merely palpitations and "pains" of the heart, digestive disturbances, constipation, or diarrhea, and headaches.

Probably sixty per cent of all patients who seek the advice of physicians are of psychopathic personality suffering mainly from what the layman characterizes with brutality as "imaginary ailments." No valid estimate has ever been made of the percentage present in the multitude who find their way into the hands of the irregular practitioners of medicine—the quacks and charlatans, and cultists. Claim of recovery of health from such ministrations—and from all religious healing as well—is virtually a confession of psychoneurosis.

Abnormality, deviation, in any one component of the personality may render an individual psychopathic and susceptible to disturbances of personality. But variation in intelligence is perhaps less prone than any other deviation to cause such unbalance, certainly far less so than disturbances in ego, or in the more deeply seated temperament and impulse life. And yet intelligence is especially the quality of personality which has caught and held the attention of parents and educators. Moreover the limitations to training, to character formation, impaired by deficiencies in intelligence, are better appreciated than for any other component of personality. For these reasons we shall here deal with intelligence in order to recapitulate in some measure the matters we have brought forward in this chapter.

Because intelligence is the component which educators chiefly recognize and toward which they direct their main efforts, the importance of its position in the personality has been grossly exaggerated. If the aim of all training and education were merely to produce brilliant scholars, then intelligence would be the main component to consider. But if, on the other hand, training and education are to aim toward the production of happily adjusted, and contented citizens, then not intelligence alone, but all the other components of personality must receive consideration. We believe even greater consideration than intelligence. This is a fact that college educators seem rarely to take into consideration and the result is seen in the failure of many college men and women to adjust themselves satisfactorily in later life.

The degree in which intelligence is present varies enormously in different personalities. It is manifest in its higher degree as the ability to think constructively in contrast to mere learning by rote. Intelligence is essential to the acquisition of knowledge, but except in inferior degrees it rises above this elementary faculty. An encyclopedic fund of information can be acquired by a small child, or by a man of moderately low intelligence, and retailed on any and all occasions. But lacking a higher degree of intelligence he can do nothing constructive with his knowledge. It remains simply a store of information.

Intelligence is the one quality of personality that can be measured with reasonable precision. Tests have been developed for this purpose and are now widely applied in "placing" children in schools, in selecting applicants for admission to colleges, and even in the employment of men in industry. A rough classification is made upon the basis of the degree of intelligence under the now-familiar designations of idiot, imbecile, moron, average intelligence, superior intelligence, and genius.

Studies of families have revealed the fact that intelligence is wholly an hereditary quality. Indeed, it follows closely the so-called Mendelian law of inheritance. A child is predestined by its inheritance to develop a certain degree of intelligence; at the moment of conception the factors are established that will endow it with superior or average intelligence or leave it a moron or an imbecile. No amount of education will increase—and fortunately neither will it decrease intelligence. What education does do is to supply information, and if it is good education, as far as intelligence is concerned, it supplies methods of correlation and application. The trained mind has learned the best and most logical methods of approaching its problems; but intelligence is required for the solution. No system has yet been devised that will do a man's thinking for him.

Some children are utterly incapable of grasping the subject-matter of the schoolroom beyond certain grades; their intellectual development has ceased at that point. Some stop at the second grade, others at the third or fifth or eighth, or some period in high school, or even some point in college. In the higher grades they are usually dropped for their scholastic failure. In the lower grades the student is not dropped for intellectual inability; legal age-limits require that the child be kept in school. Often he is retained year after year in the same classroom, not comprehending year after year the same instruction. Such a child appears often to the teacher, and the school board as well, as a total failure, an intellectual dead weight that must be tolerated in patience until he is fourteen or sixteen or whatever age the law permits his discharge from school.

Such belief and such policy is dictated by the fallacy upon which we have commented, the fallacy that education is intended to cultivate only intelligence. It is a ruinous fallacy. It is as much a fallacy as insisting that a weak and timid and resentful child shall, for the sake of his "character," year after year exploit his inferiority before the larger, stronger, and more aggressive boys on the football field. In a few progressive and hence fortunate schools the children of low intelligence are promptly diverted from intellectual pursuits and frankly trained in such useful handicrafts and avocations as fall within the scope of their intellectual ability. This most desirable step for the pupils lagging in the lower grades (and even some of the higher ones) often leads to a profound change in behavior and even to a display of an unexpected degree of intelligence.

As we have repeatedly emphasized, no component of the personality stands alone; it is merely a dependent part of an integrated whole—the structure of the complete personality. The frustration of any one component has its effect on other, perhaps on all, components of personality. The components of impulse, and temperament, and ego, may be affected by disturbances of the one component, intelligence. The disposition and total behavior are correspondingly affected. The frank recognition of the inability of the child to go beyond a certain grade, the removal of the pressure for intellectual advancement, and the substitution of vocational training, are often accompanied by a marked and favorable alteration in disposition and behavior. In short, as the environment changes the child ceases to exhibit psychopathic behavior.

By this change, not only is pressure removed from the child, pressure to accomplish the impossible, but also a dignified and agreeable way out of an unpleasant situation is provided. The child does not "lose face." Low intelligence, popular belief to the contrary, does not of necessity entail low ego regard—lack of pride. In fact, in dealing with the psychopathic individuals— and that, of course, includes nearly everyone—it is vitally important for their sake to provide what in slang is known as an "out"—an alternate value or mode of behavior that will allow the ever-present and often exquisitely sensitive ego-component to remain undisturbed. No advantage is gained by removing pressure from one component of personality and shifting it to another.

Criticism becomes constructive and beneficial instead of purely destructive if, as ill-behavior in one direction is pointed out, presumably valuable qualities in another are indicated simultaneously—an "out" provided. A partially pleasant instead of a wholly unpleasant coloring is thus given to the criticism. Even definite peculiarities of personality sometimes may be capitalized in this regard and made into matters of pride. Thus the explosive old gentleman who has been told that his irritability is a sign of a strong impulse may subsequently, after each outburst of irascibility, apologize merely so that he can say with pride that he has strong impulses, "very strong indeed"; in time the statement may, to a large extent, take the place of the outburst. The old gentleman in consequence becomes both happier and more tolerable.

With proper guidance the stupid child can say to itself in effect, "I may not be very good at studies, but I certainly know how to make boats and things. And I can stand on my head. Lots of fellows who are good at their studies can't do what I can do." The child has then found a satisfaction that removes the urge for psychopathic behavior which, in such cases, often is exhibited as a superiority in misbehavior or as an extremely negativistic attitude.

This principle applies to the adult quite as much as to the child. In the adult, however, the misbehavior may be of a less direct and obvious nature. It is more often personal. It may take the form of depressions, unreasonable irritability, or the symptoms of physical illness depending upon the inherent peculiarities of his individual personality.

There are only a few personalities so completely devoid of good qualities that it is impossible to find for them a constructive "out." It is hardly an original observation, but it remains an unfortunate fact, that it is far easier and more satisfying to criticize and scold than to praise. Scolding gives the scolder a feeling of superiority, but praise gives this pleasant feeling to the recipient. Unless a personality is extremely well balanced or extremely psychopathic, even the most minute crumbs of personal superiority are jealously cherished.

It is true that many occupations require a definite degree of intelligence; lower degrees absolutely bar success. On the other hand the requisite intelligence does not of itself assure success. The other components of personality play an important, but less easily evaluated, part toward this end. A highly intelligent man may fail completely because he has a weak impulse, lacks aggression, tires easily; even with a strong impulse he may fail because his temperamental qualities are incompatible with the situations into which his work brings him. In the next chapter there is presented the case of an intelligent and capable physician who lost his patients because of his irritable temperament. He might have lost them as readily, or even failed to gain them entirely, if the general traits of his personality had been those associated with the extreme type of leptosome physique or if he had had a marked deviation in the ego-component of his personality, or, to carry the matter even farther, if his character had been badly formed. There are a multitude of situations in which a man with any such peculiarities might succeed; there are also many in which, in spite of his intelligence, he would fail.

It is often difficult for the young college graduate to appreciate the fact that intelligence is not the sole criterion for success in the world. Intellectual accomplishment in college has been his goal and his realm of superiority, and the value by which his achievements have been judged. In the working world he sometimes finds it incomprehensible that his superiors appear to have less intelligence than he, and that other men from school, whose scholastic standing was inferior to his or who even failed to graduate, achieve success far ahead of his.

It is on this same exaggerated prestige given to intelligence that many dilettantes, who class themselves as the "intelligentsia," base their superiority. Frequently the underlying difficulty here is lack of proper character formation. This type of otherwise intelligent young gentleman and young lady has usually failed to establish definite goals of endeavor in life. With no productive outlet for their impulses, they become filled with a vague undirected tension which leads merely to restlessness. Restlessness without purpose leads to dilettantism; with purpose, to progress. They are prone to fritter away their time with more or less brilliant discussions of inconsequentials—a sort of intellectual crossword-puzzle exercise. Their psychopathic behavior often takes the form of a superiority to social convention, particularly in matters of dress, the assumption of a highly sophisticated pose, and generally a highly critical one, in regard to those of lesser intellectual brilliance. Their conversation is usually "arty" and literary. It is also generally "sappy," for the condition from which they suffer is, in effect, a sort of delayed adolescence. Such individuals are adults in years, but with the purposeless characters of adolescent youths and often with the adolescent immaturity of impulse.

Some of these intelligent psychopaths eventually find for themselves a productive place in the world—not infrequently on the editorial or art staff of "sophisticated" magazines.

Low intelligence cannot be made into high intelligence by either parental or educational pressure. But in the past, stupidity in school was assumed to arise from lack of incentive or attention. An effort was made in the home and the school to awaken incentive with punishment. Fortunately, most educators now recognize the fact that incentive is not alone a substitute for intelligence, that children—and adults also—may be incapable of carrying a burden intellectually as well as physically. But, unfortunately, to replace the whippings of an earlier day there has grown up a new and even more disturbing type of pressure—a social pressure. In the home the pressure is often based on family pride and parental competition.

If a child fails to make a place in athletics, the reason is usually obvious and, the fact accepted without protest, a suitable excuse is provided: the boy is of frail physique, he has grown too rapidly for his years, he is in the "clumsy" age, or mother objects to rough athletics. There appears to be no great family stigma attached to this aspect of competitive behavior. But if the child's grades in school are low in comparison with those of other children of his own social status, family pride is touched upon. Not infrequently the educational system is blamed, or, lacking the wide scope, the burden is borne by some particular teacher whose inefficiencies the child has disclosed to his sympathetic family. In any event the child is urged to work hard, to stay in school for mother's sake, to try and be like the neighbors' children—for "what will the neighbors think?"

Before applying such pressure the parent will be wise

to consider the whole situation as dispassionately as his own personality and character will allow him and then to proceed with caution. Pressure is certainly needed for the child of keen intellect who falls low in his scholastic work because of diverting outside activities which leave him little time for his studies. But pressure upon the intellectually inefficient is quite a different matter and a dangerous practice. It is the whip applied to the slave already bearing as large a burden as he can carry. Moreover, the parent supplied the heredity that established the stupidity of his own child. To punish the child for being like his parents may be a relief for the parent, but it is cruel to the child.

Emulation, morever, is a fallacy. Unless the personality endowments are identical, it is useless and hopeless to strive to be like others—like the neighbors' children or like Napoleon. In any event, there is always an element of danger in attempting to imitate the great and the famous in any field, war or politics or religion, but especially religion; they are nearly always markedly psychopathic, and extreme psychopaths do not make ideal models upon which to attempt to pattern the character of a normal child.

Emulation at best is a false value for self, but above all it provides a standard of comparison that makes failures the more obvious. Efforts at emulation far oftener bring disappointment, self-condemnation, and self-pity than result in solid achievement. It is more desirable and far more constructive to establish goals that are suited to the peculiarities of the individual personality than to attempt to force upon it goals that are incompatible with its qualities.

The plea to succeed in school for "mother's sake" is the cruelest and the most selfish of all weapons by which pressure is brought upon the child. A boy can bear an honest grudge after a whipping by an adult, for the adult is bigger. The boy can vent his ire in private, and even retain a certain grudging admiration for such direct and conclusive methods of applying pressure; he may even pass the matter off philosophically. Children are philosophical and rarely are their consciences wholly clear of reasons for punishment. But the responsibility inherent in the pleas of family pride and parental love allows no escape except the revocation of family ties. And family ties are graven deep in youthful character. It is from the frustration arising from such pressure applied to impressionable youths that there results some of the queerest of personality disturbances, psychopathic behavior. The case of John Nelson is typical.

John Nelson was the son of the president of one of

the country's largest and wealthiest manufacturing concerns. At the age of twenty-three, he was in the junior class in an Eastern university. He had been prepared for college in a prominent secondary school. An attack of illness had interfered with his college entrance examinations, and accordingly he was tutored intensively during the summer recess and took an additional year at the preparatory school. He entered college with a record seriously broken by recurrent illnesses, mainly gastric disturbances and general prostration of no certain diagnostic nature. It was generally assumed that, handicapped by his physical complaints, he had made the best of a school career. In college his scholastic record was low; in several instances recurrences of his ill-health at examination times necessitated reëxamination after periods of intensive tutoring. The general consensus of opinion was that while not brilliant, he was a conscientious worker and could have made a better record except for the repeated illnesses. He was popular among his fellow students. He was very proficient in the game of golf, but his low scholastic stand kept him from the college golf team.

He failed badly in the work of his junior year, and failed again on reëxamination at the end of a summer of tutoring. He became despondent, gave up his usual associations, showed marked depression, and threatened suicide.

There was no question but that the boy had an intense desire to complete his college course. His father and his two uncles had graduated from college; a sister one year older had graduated two years previously. Considerable family pressure was brought to bear on the boy, and in addition a place had been promised him in the firm as soon as he completed his college work. He was keenly interested in the business and anxious to "go to work." Except when tutoring he had spent his vacations in a minor position with the company and had given satisfaction.

On thorough examination the boy appeared to be in excellent physical condition, although he complained of headache, dizziness, indigestion, and vomiting. There appeared to be no question of the existence of the symptoms. The dizziness was so extreme as to prevent him from studying.

He was thin, but of undoubted pyknic physique; his personality appeared fairly well balanced, with only a possible question as to his intelligence. His behavior was, however, decidedly psychopathic. On previous examination his impulse was estimated as moderately strong, his temperament neither vivacious nor yet phlegmatic and with excellent resonance; the mood was predominantly cheerful, but with swings toward slight depressions. For some weeks previous to the examination he was in an extremely despondent phase, with considerable retardation of movement, so much so, in fact, that the possibility of manic-depressive illness was evident.

A study of the family history revealed that the paternal grandfather who had founded the concern was a highly intelligent and aggressive individual. The sons who now controlled the business were likewise aggressive, intelligent, and well-adjusted men. The business had prospered under their management. The boy's mother was a handsome woman of definitely pyknic physique; she was somewhat phlegmatic, was decidedly quiet, reserved, and dignified. In conversation with her it soon became obvious that her quietness and phlegmatism were consciously or unconsciously exaggerated to cover an inability to cope with any breadth of conversational topic. She was, as her husband said, a quiet "home body" whose interest in life was the care of her immediate family. With some pride he added that she was exactly like his own mother in this respect. The fact soon became apparent that in reality both the grandmother and mother were women of very moderate intelligence, but in other respects of excellent traits of personality. They had succeeded in covering their intellectual deficiency under the affection engendered from the warmth of their personalities; they were regarded as having given up their own pleasures and activities in the interest of the home life. Any imputation of lack of intelligence would have been contested upon this basis. In reality they had unconsciously taken advantage of this attitude to avoid intellectual strain. So long as they could maintain this rôle their personalities remained well adjusted.

The son, on the contrary, in whom the hereditary strain of two generations had culminated was, in his college life, faced with an actual test of his intellectual prowess; he could not retire behind the other admirable qualities of his personality, his warmth and cheerful temperament and realistic tendencies. His frustration resulted in psychopathic behavior. His avenue of escape was illness and depression. His inefficiencies had in the past been excused on that basis and opportunity given for repeated trials. With willing hands to help him he had limped through school. But here in his junior year at college he had been carried to the limit of his capabilities even with extra time and tutoring. He could go no farther.

The father was tactfully informed of the situation

and in the face of the inevitable he showed a willingness to coöperate in sparing the boy's pride and giving him a dignified way out of his difficulty. The father wrote the boy to say that his help was imperatively and immediately needed in the plant and that, although he knew the boy was anxious to finish his college career, he was asking, as a favor to him and his associates, that he drop his college work and help out at home. On receipt of this letter the boy's behavior changed at once; his symptoms of illness ceased; his depression gave place to vivacity and enthusiasm.

Eight years have passed since this episode. The young man has found his place in the company; his work, if not brilliant, is thorough and tireless and wholly satisfactory. He is an excellent handler of men and is respected by the employees. He has had no recurrence of his physical symptoms or of his depression. Ideas of suicide are remote from his mind. Neither are they likely to return as long as the business prospers.

Fortunately, he has married a young lady of distinctly superior intelligence. He scoffs good-naturedly and with some pride at her "brainy" friends and her cultural activities. His field of avocation is golf. None of her friends can compete with him there—in fact, most of her friends are ignorant of golf. He is a little sorry for them. None of his associates is more popular at the country club than he. He appears as a fine, successful man with a well-balanced and congenial personality, but with a dogged insistence that the old ways of running the plant are and will always remain the best; he wants no change. He even talks regretfully of the fact that business called him away from college; a college education is a fine thing. His sons will go to college and they will stay there till they graduate. And they probably will—thanks to their mother's intelligence.

In contrast to the case of John Nelson, that of Charles Barton shows no psychopathic behavior but does serve to illustrate some of the prevalent misconceptions in regard to intelligence—one in particular that in this instance had pathetic results.

Barton had an exceedingly well-balanced personality —his temperament was warm and cheerful, a little phlegmatic; his impulse was only moderately strong and so also was his intelligence. At the time the crisis came in his life he was thirty-three. He was ten years out of a moderately good college where he had had some difficulties in completing the work; his low scholastic standing was attributed to his wide interest in extra-curricular activities. He had been president of his class, leader of the glee club, and center on the football team, and was now one of the most loyal alumni of his *alma mater*. He always took his vacations at the time of Commencement so that he could be back for reunion. In the ten years he had acquired a wife—a leptosome in the extreme, vivacious, cold, and socially ambitious. He had also acquired, on a mortgage, a small house in the suburbs; and had developed the beautifully rotund physique of the true pyknic. His social habits were limited; his wife belonged to half a dozen afternoon clubs, was a *habitué* at auctions of antiques and a garden enthusiast. But such activities were not for Barton. A small bridge club one night a week and the movies twice—to the early show, for he needed much sleep. In fact, sleep was so insistent a function with him that he regularly dozed off at 10 P.M. in his chair even when there was "company at the house."

But he did not sleep on his job. He was a plodder with a well-defined goal toward which patiently and persistently he directed all his efforts. He was executive foreman of the hardware department of a large manufacturing company. Some day he would be superintendent. His ideals rose no higher; he knew his own limitations; he did not aspire to be president or even general manager. But superintendent he would be. His work was highly satisfactory—it was satisfactory by dint of unremitting plodding.

And then the crisis came. His wife "worked on him" for a solid week to get him to attend an evening lecture sponsored by one of her clubs. She was on the speakers' committee. And the speaker was to talk on "Psychology of Success." To the psychologists and to all successful men it may be said that the speaker was neither, but his pose and manners and his language were—as all the ladies agreed—"just too fascinating."

Charles Barton went to the lecture. There he listened to a polished exposition in which the speaker for forty-five minutes—his contract called for an additional fifteen minutes for questions—elaborately hitched his horse backwards to the cart. The gist of his message was this: successful men, men of high position, are marked by the wide scope of their interests and activities. This fact he demonstrated with the careless shuffle of famous names. Such-and-such, the great banker, not only was director in eleven institutions, but was also a city executive, a member of the school board, prominent in the social-service organization, and a devotee of golf. So-and-so, the financial wizard, controlled his own philanthropies, was an after-dinner speaker of more than national repute, went to Washington each week to advise the government, traveled a hundred thousand miles a year on business, and knew every detail of the working of the great corporation under his control. There, said the speaker, in effect, is the formula for success—wide activity. Wide activity widens the mind; the widened mind has great capacity for accomplishment. And ergo success.

Perhaps the speaker's sophistry was less apparent amid his flow of "fine language" than in our brief and blunt statements. The activities of these great men sounded fine to Barton. He had not quite enough intelligence to sort out the fallacy—the fact that these men over whose names the speaker's tongue rolled with such intimacy were, unlike him, men of vast energy and vast intelligence. They could do their jobs with dispatch and without plodding; they had time and energy left for a dozen more jobs besides. They were born that way. Barton was not. But after all he had been a big man in college, and certainly his activities were wide there. There was some truth in what the "fellow" said. After two weeks of thinking over the problem, Barton made his decision. He joined two clubs, ran for and was elected second selectman of his suburban village, was given a position on the school board and the newly-founded zoning commission. In all these positions he worked hard, plodded meticulously over the details. He was a great success in his widened affairs, but he lost his position at the factory. Barton couldn't do both jobs at the same time—he lacked the intelligence. He was a plodder.

Now when Barton was discharged he did not, like John Nelson in his college dilemma, develop symptoms of disease as evasion of responsibility. Barton had a well-balanced personality; he had made a mistake and he knew it and he knew why. He hunted for a new job and got it. He is now foreman of his department. He has his ambitions fixed on the superintendency. Some day he will get it.

Low intelligence—popular belief to the contrary—does not of itself affect the balance of the personality. Disturbance occurs only when an unbearable strain is forced upon a deficient intelligence, when unachievable goals are set for it and when insight is lacking.

The fact of the matter is that there are probably more "normal" personalities among those of low than among those of high intelligence. High intelligence sets high goals for achievement which require strong qualities in all the components of personality. The moron, striving for his own lowly goals, often has the other moderate qualities of personality to assure success and satisfaction. He frequently finds a most congenial environment, one that makes little strain upon his intellect and in which he is admirably adjusted. He is then a contented and useful citizen.

For peace of mind much is to be said in favor of the old European system of traditional class employment, so distasteful to American concepts of personal achievement. The butler, the gardener, the parlor maid, the seamstress, the clerk, each come of a long family line in these same occupations. Son like father, like grandfather; that is the way inheritance is transmitted; that is the way intelligence is passed. Under the traditional system the intelligence and a compatible goal were established simultaneously. The environment was accepted and peace of mind was secured.

Under a contrary system such as our own, with its heritage of pioneer struggles, a continual pressure is exerted for self-betterment, self-advancement through emulation. The results are a few striking successes—very few—and many failures. A few men succeed in raising themselves to high positions; many thousands strive pitifully and fail, and they are broken by their failures. Their discontent, their frustration, often appears as some form of psychopathic behavior.

And finally, well-balanced and well-adjusted individuals of low intelligence are not limited to the "working-classes." Some of the most popular and vivacious débutantes fresh from the grooming of the finishing-school, some of the most charming hostesses of prominent families, some of the most lovable and gracious gentlemen of leisure, possess a degree of intelligence that places them in the moron class. Intelligence as a quality of personality may be admired and respected by others, but it is not intelligence that makes for love and popularity and good companionship. These appealing qualities are to be found in certain aspects of temperament and ego and impulse.

PART IV

BONDAGE IN MOODS AND EMOTIONS

Chapter IV

BONDAGE IN MOODS AND EMOTIONS

TEMPERAMENT is the sum-total of all the emotional qualities of the individual; his sensations and his reactions; what he feels and how he responds.

To no aspect of personality does the ancient admonition "know thyself" apply with more force than to temperament. Know temperament. And knowing it, discount the perversions, the distortions, the falsifications caused by moods and emotions. Thus and thus only can one be brought into contact with actualities.

Temperament stands between each man and his surroundings. It is through his individual temperament that he must always see and feel the world about him—experience it. Each of his perceptions is colored by this temperament.

Each man is endowed by heredity with individual and permanent qualities of temperament. In these qualities there are enormous variations. Some men are born to be cheerful and some gloomy; others irritable, and still others anxious; some men are born to be vivacious and some phlegmatic; some to be cold and some to be warm. These inherent qualities can not be altered. But the misrepresentation they produce in perception can be discounted. And their display can be controlled. They must first be recognized and understood.

The qualities of his temperament are to an individual as colored glasses before his eyes. He can never discard them; only through them can he see the world. If the glass is clouded, to him the world is drab; if the glass is bent or twisted, his vision is perverted. But since the individual has never seen except through the glasses, that is the way the world is to him. It is thus that he sees it. Why should he doubt his perceptions?

Doubt comes only when he realizes that his own temperament colors and perverts all his perceptions. Understanding follows when he learns his peculiarities. For then he can discount them. He can say in effect: "The world fills me with anxiety, but part of this anxiety is in my own temperament. I have no real cause for anxiety. This sensation of anxiety is merely my individual peculiarity. As such it is to be discounted or disregarded."

When a man can act upon this knowledge he has taken the first steps toward self-improvement; he has moved toward the fulfillment of the purpose inherent in the admonition "know thyself."

On the one side temperament is rooted in the flesh of the body; stimuli continually arising within the body act upon it. On the other side temperament is in contact with the environment; stimuli continually arising from the outside act upon it. The stimuli from both sources are integrated—blended together—in the temperament. The man experiences neither the sensations coming from the outside nor those coming from the inside; he experiences only the total sensation blended from the two. Thus in all his perceptions a part is played by his individuality. His perceptions and his reactions are made in response to sensations that he alone can experience—sensations determined by his temperament.

An identical sensation coming from the outside causes different reactions in different men. One man may respond in quiet cheerfulness; another with trembling anxiety; and still another with explosive rage; and so on throughout the entire range of temperamental qualities. Each man reacts according to his individual temperament. Temperament is revealed in responses.

But it does not follow from these facts that the nature of the sensation received from the outside is identical in all individuals viewing the same occurrence. Quite

[131]

the contrary. It is here that values set by acquired character come into play. Character determines in part the strength and nature of the sensation drawn from the occurrence. Men, quite independently of temperamental qualities, may view the same occurrence in entirely different lights.

Thus three individuals in court watching a fourth being sentenced to prison derive different sensations from the scene if one is the prisoner's mother, another his accuser, and the third a disinterested spectator. Each sets different values on the situation. These values are inherent in the character that each has acquired.

And yet all mothers, all enemies, and all spectators will not behave identically in such a situation. One mother may sit in stolid silence; another scream in uncontrollable excitement; or fall into a silent faint. One accuser may show a malicious satisfaction; another sorrow and compassion. One spectator may be unmoved except in curiosity; another avert his face in horror. In the total sensation that each experiences and in the reaction that each makes, there is one unaltered individual constant—the inherent temperamental qualities of each person. These temperamental qualities are felt and they are shown. They can be observed and they can be identified. They can even be classified.

For this classification of individual temperaments it is not necessary to study the behavior of men in extreme or tragic situations. The qualities of temperament in every individual are experienced and shown in every situation of daily life.

The specific qualities of temperament which afford a basis for classification are tempo, mood, and resonance (depth of feeling). All three are present in every temperament; but as between individual temperaments they differ widely in quality and degree. One temperament may show a tempo that is phlegmatic, a mood that is gloomy, a resonance that is deep (warm). Another may be vivacious, anxious, cold; still another explosive, changeable, warm. In each case, and in all other possible ones, the combinations of inherent qualities serve to characterize the temperament.

MOOD

Every man expresses continually his satisfaction or dissatisfaction with the sensations he experiences. This expression is called his mood. It is established at any instant by the sum-total of the blended sensations coming from the inside and from the outside of the body. In response to changes in the external sensations the mood alters from moment to moment; the man accordingly

[133]

appears pleased or annoyed, angry or depressed. But in each case the sensation and its expression are equally influenced by internal sensations. Beneath, indeed, within, all these fluctuations, there is a constant and general fundamental mood derived from the constant internal sensations. The man is accordingly prevailingly cheerful, or gloomy, or irritable, or anxious. On receiving an unpleasant external sensation the cheerful man is made less cheerful, while the gloomy is cast into deeper dejection, the irritable flies into a rage, and the anxious is filled with apprehension.

It is this fundamental mood that characterizes temperament. The sensations which establish the mood arise from the activities of the cells of which the body is constituted. Mood reflects the essential harmony or disharmony of fundamental vital processes. And these processes are in turn dependent upon hereditary structural endowment.

Fundamental moods are altered only by altering the vital activities of the body, by injury or disease, or poisoning. But it does not follow that cheerfulness is a sign of good health and that gloom is a sign of disease. Illness has its transient influence on mood, but only in degree. The cheerful man when ailing becomes less cheerful, but at his worst he never reaches the depths to which the gloomy man descends. His normal cheerfulness reasserts itself during convalescence, while the gloomy man then becomes merely less aggressive in his gloom.

The gravest injuries, a broken back, even, may cause no serious alteration in moods. Less alteration in fact than may occur from a head cold, for infection interferes more with general bodily processes than does a local injury.

On the other hand, diseases that seriously disturb the vital processes—diseases that interfere with the circulation of blood, with the digestion of food, with respiration, or with the delicate adjustment of the glands of internal secretion, may influence mood profoundly, sometimes permanently.

It is a curious fact, noted many years ago, that diseases of the lungs and heart are often accompanied by anxiety, while diseases of the abdominal organs are accompanied by gloom. There is the pessimism of the dyspeptic. The restriction of the flow of blood due to hardening of the arteries, with the accompanying curtailment of oxygen to the cells, frequently gives rise to a permanent mood of irritability. This is a change that is common in old age. A similar though transient effect may occur from shortage of oxygen due to high altitude, as in an aeroplane flight or a mountain climb. Many women, as the result of the bodily changes occurring during menstruation, changes primarily due to alteration in the activity of glands of internal secretion, show temporary alteration in their prevailing moods. Usually they become irritable or unstable. Even more striking are the mood changes that, for a similar reason, may occur at the period of the menopause.

The bodily disturbances, functional or organic, caused by poisons such as alcohol, tobacco, coffee, tea, or other drugs, have their effects on mood. Some are temporary and some permanent. The exhilaration that results from alcohol passes into gloom and depression with returning sobriety. Both effects arise from a temporary disorganization of cellular activity. When the effect has passed, the normal mood again prevails. The depression and sense of anxiety often associated with excessive smoking usually disappear when the tobacco is curtailed. But there are limits to cellular tolerance; when taken in prolonged excess alcohol or drugs may leave a permanent mark both upon physical structure and upon mood.

TEMPO

The same basic processes that establish the fundamental mood also establish the tempo of temperament.

But mood is not emotion; it is the coloring given to it.

Emotion means literally a movement or stirring up; it is the stirring up of the activities of the flesh. Every stimulus from the outside, be it slight or great, is echoed by a response in the flesh, not necessarily a response shown in movement, but always a response directed toward movement. If the stimulus is strong, some of the actual bodily changes resulting are detectable; the heart beats faster and breathing is quickened; the pressure of the blood in the arteries rises; sugar is poured into the blood to act as a fuel for the expected exertion; and the muscles tighten and become tense.

The sensation experienced by a man in any emotional reaction is that of an inner tension; the greater the reaction the greater the tension. And this tension seeks relief in muscular movement. Talking, crying, laughing, trembling, gesticulating, and clapping the hands are as much muscular movement, and hence relief from tension, as are fighting or running.

But the tension resulting from emotion is undifferentiated and undirected. It merely seeks relief, seeks to be discharged in movement. Mood imparts to the tension a pleasant or unpleasant feeling. This feeling gives direction to the discharge. Thus when the tension is

[137]

relieved it is displayed as anger, irritability, quarrelsomeness, or cheerfulness, according to the qualities of the prevailing mood.

In some men the inner tension develops much more rapidly than in others; some are more excitable and hence more responsive than others. There are many reasons to believe that this difference in excitability is determined by the functioning of glands of internal secretion; by the rate and ease with which they discharge their products into the blood. These features in turn depend largely upon hereditary endowment. Not one but many glands take part in the general process of developing the inner tension of emotion, but one in particular, the thyroid gland, located at the base of the neck, has a direct influence upon excitability.

This gland is subject to the disturbances from which definite diseases result. And one of the most striking features of these disturbances is the profound change in the emotional life. If the gland produces less than the normal amount of secretion, the disease myxedema results. The individual so affected may be changed from a vivacious person into one who is phlegmatic, slow of movement and of thought, indifferent to his surroundings, unexcitable, unemotional. Administering precisely determined amounts of the extract made from the thyroid gland of some animal such as the sheep, causes the symptoms of the disease to disappear; the emotional life is restored to normal.

If, in contrast to the condition of myxedema, the gland secretes too abundantly, the disease known as exophthalmic goiter results and an entirely opposite emotional effect is produced. Intense excitement is experienced; the heart throbs; the eyes bulge, giving the face an expression of fear; the muscles quiver so that the tongue and fingers tremble; there is vivacity of speech and movement that rises to great heights on slight provocation. The symptoms of the disease may be relieved, the excitement quieted, by removing surgically a portion of the gland. These same symptoms may also be produced even in severe form in the normal individual by swallowing the thyroid extract used with such benefit in the treatment of myxedema.

The fact that some men are inherently more excitable than others makes it possible to classify them on this basis into two broad groups—the emotive and the phlegmatic. Among the emotive further classification is possible from the fact that the inner tension which they all experience in high degree has different modes of discharge.

In some the tension is relieved immediately and more

or less constantly in quick movement and rapid, abundant speech. Such individuals are classed as the *vivacious*.

In others the tension is discharged far less easily and less purposefully. It is experienced acutely, but it is dammed back from articulate expression and directed instead into involuntary channels, trembling, muscular tension, crying, and the like. Such individuals are classed as the *excitable*.

In others the tension is not relieved continuously, nor is it shown, but is accumulated until it breaks forth in a violent discharge, an explosion, usually of anger. Such individuals are classed as the *explosive*.

There are still others in whom the tension also accumulates, but to a less extent, and is discharged more frequently. It is always colored by an unpleasant inner feeling, a disagreeable mood. Such individuals are classed as the *irritable*.

Among the emotive, there are all degrees of excitability and unexcitability. Some men are so vivacious, so excitable, or so explosive that they appear distinctly abnormal. Their temperamental peculiarity overshadows all other qualities of their personality and becomes its main distinguishing feature.

Other men are so phlegmatic that they are sodden, torpid, almost vegetable-like in their unresponsiveness.

With them also their extreme trait is the characterizing feature of their personalities.

The great majority of men, however, fall between these extremes. But the average man is rarely so completely balanced in tempo of temperament that he does not incline toward one extreme or the other. He will exhibit some of the temperamental peculiarities that characterize the behavior of the individuals in the cases to be given here. The points of similarity permit his classification.

In these cases emphasis is put upon the display of temperamental traits. But it must be borne in mind that what is really being described is total behavior and that in each instance the behavior is shaped not only by the peculiarities of temperament, but also by the peculiarities of impulse, intelligence, ego, character, and environment. This fact of necessity applies to all cases given in this book, regardless of the feature we seek to demonstrate. Here we have attempted, as far as our material would permit, to select individuals in whom the components of behavior other than temperament show no marked deviation from the normal. Likewise the environments are commonplace.

The Vivacious.—The vivacious are distinguished by their continual play of movement. They are always active. Their movements are rapid. They speak in quick tempo. They gesture not only to their own remarks, but frequently to those of others as well.

With well-formed characters the vivacious may be enormously productive; but without this direction to their energies they are apt to be mere busybodies.

The weakness of this temperament lies in its acute awareness to its surroundings and its immediate responsiveness. In consequence the vivacious are prone to distractiveness, fickleness, superficiality, and often to expansiveness as well.

Take the case of Mr. Pebbles:

He is an intelligent, successful, and very vivacious man. He lives in the suburbs; his nine acres he calls an estate; it is ten miles from his office, two miles from the country club, ten blocks from the nearest church. He prefers to walk if he must go to church. All the way there and back he is three feet ahead of his wife, oblivious to her entreaties to walk more slowly. All his life people have been trying to catch up to him. In church he has found it hard to sit still and so he has become a vestryman. He is through passing the plate before any of the others, and while he waits for them, he jingles the coins he has collected. It is not nervousness; it's just that he cannot be still.

At dinner he is first through each course, and so disturbs the more leisurely diners by fidgeting with his forks and spoons and rocking back and forth in his chair, not because of ignorance of social amenities—he just cannot help it. He can't sit still; he is an inveterate "fidgeter"; if he must listen to some one else, he squirms in his chair and beats an incessant devil's tattoo on its arms. He must either move or talk. Often he has nothing essential to say, merely a flow of words. But he will talk at any time to anyone who will serve as an audience—that is, anyone except "old" Mrs. Jenkins, who descends on his wife at times bursting with chatter and gossip. He cannot stand her. He calls her an old busybody. He would dislike her even more if he knew that the neighbors said that he and she were two of a kind.

He is no gossip, just chatty, but of course at times he says far more than is wise. It is not advisable to trust him with a secret, for it will surely pop out in the flow of words. His stories are good ones; at least he makes a good story out of every triviality. And he is convincing, too, very sure of himself.

He is active in civic affairs; in fact he is active in any field that catches his interest. He heads the civic betterment committee of his town. He presents plans to that modest body which involve an expense beyond the means of the community. Some one has to hold him in check and so quiet but determined Mrs. Burton is always put on the same committees with him. And he is on many; others are too slow to act. "Here, let me do it." That is his slogan.

He wrote the play for the community show. (Some of the audience said it was plagiarized, but all admitted it had movement.) He sold more tickets than anyone on the committee. He tried to direct the show, and played the leading character.

At home he plays the leading character also. His children find it difficult to amuse themselves when he is there. He disarranges all their plans. He gets up a swimming-party and a picnic while they are trying to make up their minds to go to a dance. "You don't want to dance," he says; "too nice a day to stay indoors." He provides the food for the picnic; there is enough for ten. No one touches the chocolate cake, for he has brought pie and ice-cream, candy and cookies.

His oldest daughter, Alice, is nearly as vivacious as he is. His wife wishes he wouldn't encourage her in her brief visits at home. "Poor mother" doesn't know what to do with them when they are both in the house; there is not a moment of peace and quiet. The servants are utterly ruined. Neither one of the two lets them do a thing. They both rush from the dinner table to the telephone when it rings, although it is two rooms away; they continue their conversations shouting back to the other after they have removed the receiver.

Mrs. Pebbles has an even worse time when her husband brings home guests—and that is often. To her it seems that he uses no discretion in choosing his friends. He mixes his company frightfully and calls everyone by his first name. Many of his guests never return, for most are exhausted after a day at the estate. He walks them to every corner of his nine acres; shows them all over the house (to his wife's great discomfort, especially when there are ladies in the party). She can't understand where on earth he gets so many new friends, when they have so many old ones. But she knows he will soon drop them and acquire others.

At home, even without company, he is something of a trial. He's a nighthawk—last one to bed and the first one up, a noisy riser, singing and clattering in the bathroom. It's a relief when he goes out of the house, except that his wife is worried about the drive to town. She knows he will be killed some day. He never slows down for curves and as for staying in line, that is more of a detail than he can stand. Most drivers on the road think he is inconsiderate, and his passengers think he is reckless. His wife's only relief is that he refuses to drive far on Saturday and Sunday or other holidays, because it takes too long to get anywhere in the traffic.

Everyone at the office knows when he arrives. He is up the stairs in ten long strides. The door is either slammed or left open. He has no time to stop and close it; he is halfway across the room, giving orders to his secretary. He has had four secretaries this year. One had what she called a nervous breakdown. He sent her to a sanitarium he knew well. He seems to know everything. At least, if anything happens he has a remedy for it. It may not be the right one, but he never hesitates to offer it.

His letters are long; his business reports wordy; his plans numerous and expansive, but not always sound. He can't be bothered with details. Details are not important; it's the big things that count; let some one who has nothing else to do look out for the details. That is his way of tackling a job. And he has tackled a thousand and one that are still unfinished or forgotten.

He combined a business trip abroad with his vacation: he took his wife and his oldest daughter. They were a sore trial for Mrs. Pebbles. She was embarrassed by the friends they made on the boat and the invitations they gave to visit them at home. Everywhere

Mr. Pebbles tipped freely, too freely, but then he wanted results. His baggage must get off the boat first, even if others are offended and his wife ashamed. They had planned to visit Paris with a group from the boat, but the others dropped out after the first day and took a rest. The Louvre, Notre Dame, Montmartre, Montparnasse—two days in Paris. They could see the rest on the way back if they wanted to, and so they took a swift car to Versailles and then on to Germany. Europe was done in three weeks, and everything photographed.

Mrs. Pebbles rested all the way back on the boat. When the family landed, even Mr. Pebbles was amazed at the array of knickknacks they had to declare. But for his wife the worst of that trip were those thousands of feet of film; she has to see them over and over in the darkened library for each new group of friends. Mr. Pebbles always speeds up the projecting machine until Europe shows on the screen with the same jerk and blur in which that visit will always remain in his wife's memory.

Now, of course, no reader will number among his acquaintances one who acts precisely as Mr. Pebbles does. But if he knows a vivacious man or woman, and certainly he does, he will see in his or her traits a sufficient similarity to those of Mr. Pebbles to recognize the classification of vivacious. The traits that serve as clues are often little ones; the talkativeness, the restlessness, the inability to sit still, the fumbling with the table silver, the distractability. All arise from the one feature that characterizes the vivacious; the constant release of a quickly mounting inner tension.

Deliberately in writing of Mr. Pebbles we have centered our attention on his play of emotions; as given here mood is not a prominent feature of his temperamental makeup. But it might have been.

Many of the vivacious are cheerful. With a cheerful mood Mr. Pebbles would have been an aggressive optimist showing a height of spirits that is pleasant, perhaps, but not always infectious—not a wholly comfortable cheerfulness. And yet there are occasionally cheerful vivacious individuals who are as quick of wits as they are quick of motion; they are the natural-born mimics and comedians whose flights into the absurd are irresistibly amusing. But sometimes when they fall a little short in their efforts, they are merely aggressive "show-offs" and bores.

If Mr. Pebbles were of anxious mood, his feeling of panic would be spread wherever he went. His very vivacity would force it upon others. But he would be at his worst if he were endowed with a mood of irri-

THE SUSPICIOUS MAN
"Is the bar put to the hall door?"
From the English translation of the "Characters"
of Theophrastus

tability, for his unpleasant inner feeling would be vented in every contact of his active life. If his irritability took the form of quarrelsomeness, he would keep not only himself, but also his family, his employees, and his neighbors simmering in hot water all the time.

We have said nothing of the effects of alcohol on Mr. Pebbles; the fact is that he did not drink. But if he had, he would have borne the alcohol badly. All of the vivacious do. It increases the play of their emotions; their vivacity is heightened often almost to a state of frenzy. The vivacious are, as O. Henry said, in regard to one of his Irish characters, half drunk when they are sober.

The sympathy of Mr. Pebbles toward other people, his depth of feeling, his resonance, could at best be only superficial. The vivacious may be very cold, but they are never very warm. Their distractability keeps them from concentrating such sympathies as they have for long on one subject. One does not confide readily in the extremely vivacious; they interrupt; they know the story before it is half told; they want to do all the talking themselves; they have no time to listen; they usually get off the subject; they generally end by talking about themselves.

The Excitables.—Mr. Pebbles was easily excited; in

fact, nearly everything excited him to speech and motion. But he was not a true excitable. He differed from the excitable in both the quality and the expression of his inner tension. In the first place his tension corresponded, but in high degree, to the cause of the excitement. In the second place it was relieved immediately in purposeful motions. His actions were merely exaggerations of those that wholly normal men might exhibit under similar circumstances. When they smiled, he laughed; when they hurried, he rushed; and when they became mildly enthusiastic in greeting a friend, he was carried to transports of back-slapping and arm-pumping.

In the excitable, on the contrary, the inner tension builds up into sudden gusts and squalls that carry it to heights out of all proportion to the cause of the excitement. Nor does the tension find a ready relief in purposeful action; instead, dammed back, it is experienced as tension, a tension that shakes and racks the flesh.

The vivacious man talks, fidgets, and taps his fingers; the excitable man becomes tense and wrings his hands.

A normal man, confronted by an unusual and terrifying situation, may yield to a panic of emotion. His tension may then flow into involuntary channels; he may pale and blush, perspire, tremble, cry, even faint. But the excitable experiences these same sensations and shows these same signs of unrelieved tension even when the situation is one that would not be unusual or terrifying to the normal man, only mildly exciting, perhaps pleasantly so.

The excitable lacks a balance wheel to his actions. He is the counterpart of the child who becomes sick with the excitement of a birthday party and of the woman who in fits of "hysterics" sobs and screams and throws her belongings on the floor. The excitable is the first to cry "fire" at the theater and rush blindly for an exit. He is likewise the "wild man," easily goaded to rage, who rushes madly amuck, striking, kicking, clawing, screaming.

Fortunately, most excitables have their moments of calm. Their excitement usually dies out as quickly as it rises. But there are some who remain for long periods at a time in a state of high emotional tension. They will start and cry out at any sudden noise.

The excitables are not all quick and active; many of them appear almost phlegmatic in the slowness of their normal speech and the clumsiness of their movements. When their tension rises; they may become inarticulate, stuttering and spluttering; their arms twitch and legs and head twist in purposeless gestures.

The excitable can never fully school himself to control his nervous tension; but if he is intelligent and persevering, he can learn to control its manifestations, to discount his excitement.

Thus Elbert Curley is an excitable, but there are few people who know it. His manner seems at times stiff and unnatural, but rarely does anyone sense the storms of excitement covered by his rigidity, his aloofness, and his studied calm. Today at the age of fifty-three, and under quite a different name from the one we have given him, he is an internationally known newspaper correspondent and lecturer. His true name would be familiar to every reader.

There were times when Elbert Curley could not hide his feelings. He does not look back with pleasure at his childhood. He can remember all too vividly the emotional panics that he could not then hold in check.

The dogs on the street of the small town where he lived frightened him; they frightened nearly all the other children, for that matter, but they could run and when they were safely behind fences, they could laugh and go on with their games. But not Elbert; he couldn't run; he stood rigid and screamed. When his mother or his nurse came to his rescue—and Elbert was rarely far from nurse or mother—he grasped her hand and sobbed and shook.

On such days, and they were many, he could not eat. The reaction from his fright nauseated him; filled his throat with a "lump," so that he couldn't swallow. Sometimes he had a fever, and the family doctor was called in to see him. But the doctor "frightened" him. It wasn't that he was afraid of the kindly old physician; but his mere presence made Elbert pant and tremble. He would shrink away from the gentle hand like a frightened animal. But the doctor was tactful: there was nothing to worry about; Elbert was simply a delicate, high-strung child, "nervous," like his mother.

The neighbors thought the mother simply spoiled. She had the whole family literally tiptoeing about her. A sudden noise gave her a headache; trouble with the servants sent her to bed; a social engagement exhausted her—and it did literally. A word of criticism, a slight, a rebuff, and she fled home with a panted excuse. When she gave the lawn party for the church and the table with the ice-cream collapsed, she screamed, ran into the house and locked the door. Mrs. Falham had seen her through the window throw herself on the bed and beat her fists against the spread.

Why, with such childish goings-on, if the preacher's

wife hadn't stepped into the breach and straightened out the mess, the whole party would have been a failure. But then Clara Curley's ways were known to everyone. It was just Clara's nerves. The other women sometimes wondered how she had ever gone through the ordeal of bearing her children; and she was such a flighty prude they even wondered how she got them.

But at any rate there was Elbert—with his mother's nerves. He was making a bad time of it in his first years at school. On the playground when the other children took him into their games he was hopeless and helpless; he quivered with excitement, ran wildly, but in the wrong direction, fumbled and fell. In the schoolroom he was regarded by his teachers as timid, very timid and shy. He was difficult to handle.

Everyone thought Elbert easily embarrassed; but in reality he wasn't. True embarrassment, self-consciousness, has its source in ego, in fact in a weakness of the ego. Elbert had a healthy ego. It wasn't embarrassment that made him stammer and tremble; it was the gusts of inner tension that he could feel, but for which he could find no relief. The mere anticipation that he was to be called on to recite swept him with a wave of nausea and brought the tears to his eyes.

It was the tears especially that were Elbert's chagrin;

a kind word and a pat on the back and the tears would flow; a word in scolding, a threat of any sort, and they would flow again. If on the street a stranger stopped him to ask for some simple information Elbert might shake his head or he might cry. He did not know why he cried. And if he were asked, he simply cried the more.

Elbert was not a coward, but the tears made a coward of him. The slightest move toward him in play, the slightest antagonism among his fellows, and Elbert wept. The tears made him angry. His anger made him weep. To hide his tears he ran. His antagonists ran after him. Elbert was chased home every day from school by boys smaller than he. The injustice of the situation added to his excitement. He suffered as only the emotional can suffer.

A turning-point in his early career came on one of his evening runs from school. He stumbled and fell. His antagonist merely in a teasing spirit pounced upon him. It was the antagonist's mistake. Elbert wept and Elbert screamed, but Elbert also fought and according to no known rules. He bit, he clawed, and struck in a blind wave of uncontrollable emotion. He was finally pried off of his battered adversary by one of the larger boys, upon whom Elbert turned, still clawing, biting, and kicking. Alone he held the field. And then the revulsion set in; he made his way home weak and trembling, nauseated. He went without his dinner that night, but he came home from school in peace the next day.

As Elbert grew older, his emotions stood in the way of every stage of his development. Girls, parties, picnics, clubs, outings, camps, each was a struggle with his "nerves." At first he tried to avoid new situations, but if faced with them his unstable emotions carried him away into shrill laughter, wild motions, extravagant behavior. He made a fool of himself and was old enough now to know it. He suffered, but he was also learning to disguise his feelings.

He wanted beyond all else to show the sangfroid of his less excitable friends. He drove himself in a sort of discipline to accomplish every act of bravery that his fellows showed. At the swimming-pool he watched the others dive in tense emotion; and then without their joyous laughing, but instead with set face and with rigid steps, he climbed the diving ladder one rung higher than they had climbed. He could do it. But the tension was still there; racking him. And he could do it if he fixed his attention on each rung and gripped it tightly. Almost without looking at the water he would dive. It was a stiff and awkward dive, but it was high. His

[158]

very silence, his tense abstraction, gave the impression of calm indifference. Only his dilated pupils, his stiff legs, his short, gasping breaths through tightened lips gave the clues to the inner tension that he hid.

The same self-discipline that made him climb to a higher rung on the diving ladder made him take up public speaking. In his school days it was public speaking—declamation they called it then—that was his greatest burden. As his turn to mount the platform neared, his inner tension rose until he was breathless and nearly inarticulate. But he spoke. And today, in adult years as a professional lecturer, each appearance is still a repetition of those schoolroom episodes—a daily ordeal of stage fright.

It begins on the train; it grows with each mile that brings him nearer to his destination. He is silent, almost morose, not infrequently rude to his host and hostess; his manner abstract, remote; his mind is on the ordeal before him; his flesh tingles with suppressed emotion. In the presence of his audience he could scream, he could run; but no one in the audience sees through his stiff disguise. Only in his voice is there a threat of emotion; it is disquieting perhaps to his phlegmatic listeners, but compelling always. He is referred to as enthusiastic and sincere.

Elbert Curley has control for most situations; but on rare occasions it deserts him. The last time was fifteen years ago. It was then that his wife bore him his first child. Elbert fainted in the corridor of the hospital. His wife's nurse left her patient to revive him; the obstetrician mercifully gave him the injection of sedative that had been prepared for his wife.

Some excitables find sedatives helpful in calming their inner tension. But for them alcohol is not a sedative. The excitables, like the vivacious, bear alcohol badly. Even in small amounts it destroys such control as they have developed. The sociable drink has uncovered many an excitable, often to the discomfort of the host. Some excitables find that smoking—not the tobacco itself, but the motions of smoking—helps to hide their nervousness. But this very nervousness in turn often makes them smoke excessively; under strain they may smoke incessantly.

Elbert Curley, deprived of the control that he has developed, would present a different type of behavior—the type that his mother showed. But not all excitables exercise the control that he does; and many do not try. Intelligence, mood, and ego each play a part, in shaping the display of the emotional tension. With low intelligence and a cheerful mood Elbert Curley might have been a jittery fool, the lifelong butt of every practical joker. With irritable mood his spells of excitement might have taken the form of unpredictable and uncontrollable rages. Many cold tyrants whose reigns have been marked by wanton atrocities have had in common with the "calm" Elbert Curley and the hysterical Clara Curley an excitable temperament. But the saddest temperamental combination that can come to any man is excitability colored with a mood of anxiety. To such a man each trivial occurrence is a devastating source of apprehension. No one with such a temperament could ever doubt the truth of the statement: "Our sorrows are born within us."

The Explosive.—The explosive is distinguished from excitable by the fact that he has a definite outlet for the tension that develops within him. He is distinguished from the vivacious by the fact that the discharge is not immediate. His tension builds up, reaches a high point, and is then relieved in a sudden violent discharge. Often the occurrence which precipitates the discharge appears quite insignificant; the violence of the reaction seems out of all proportions. The explosion is the discharge of a tension accumulated from previous occurrences.

Furthermore, outbursts of the explosive are not the temper-tantrum of the child or of the man or woman who has not quite grown up, nor yet of the man who works up a temper to scare people and gain his own ends and who takes a pride in having a bad temper. Tantrums are explosions, but they are of value to the actor who stages them. The child who yells and squalls and obtains a toy instead of a spanking, and the lady who storms or even sulks to obtain her way, get value for their efforts. Their manifestations belong not primarily in the field of temperament, but in that of character. For the true explosive there is no thought of gainful value attached to his outbursts; indeed, they are more often than not costly to him.

Thus it was with Charles Kelly. He was the outstanding athlete in his college, but he failed to become captain of the football team because of his ungovernable temper. He was not unsportsmanly and he was a good loser. But during a game with the team from another college, with the score well against his own, he was tackled heavily near the goal line. On rising he shook his fist at his opponent. The members of his own team held him and tried to calm him. On the next run the same opponent tackled him again. This time he struck. And when the referee penalized his team, he suddenly struck the official as well. He was ordered from the game. This episode enacted before some 50,000 spectators was merely the culmination of many similar minor occurrences.

Charles likewise failed to make the best fraternity. His social background was excellent; he came of an old and wealthy New York family. In his relations with the other students he was usually affable, but during a friendly card game in which he chafed with growing irritation at a run of ill luck, an opponent chanced to ask if he had reneged. Instead of replying to the question, he rose abruptly with a curse, swept the cards from the table, and left the room, slamming the door after him. On a similar occasion he had struck his opponent for an equally trivial matter. Three times he had been in trouble with the police for using abusive language to officers who stopped him in his car for minor traffic infractions. His classmates avoided, as far as possible, having friendly tussles with him, for what commenced as horse play he often turned into a serious battle. When enraged he strikes blindly with any object that comes to hand.

Charles was only moderately intelligent, but managed to make passing grades in his studies. He came close, however, to being expelled at the time of an examination in English. Irritated at the type of questions asked, he wrote fast and almost unintelligibly, then rose abruptly, tore his papers in half, threw them on the floor and left the room.

The explosiveness, so costly in the values which Charles Kelly cherished, is seen in minor degree in many athletic contests, even in friendly games of golf and tennis: the contestant who breaks his golf club on the ground after missing a series of shots, the one who suddenly throws his racket down and curses after a bad serve, and even the one from whom a violent "damn" bursts when he returns a shot into the net.

Many efficient and highly productive men are explosive. Their explosiveness seems to add to the forcefulness of their personalities and to be a part of the aggressiveness to which they owe their success.

Thus Guy Lawrence became the sales manager of a corporation having agencies in every large city in the United States. The president, who, previous to his arrival, had controlled matters of organization and personnel, was a very intelligent man highly trained in the technical aspects of his business; he had maintained the investments of the company in excellent order, but competition had cut into sales seriously; the company was doing much less business than it should. In this situation Lawrence was called in to furnish "new blood."

Changes were apparent at once, and for a time the business was in a turmoil. His first move was to visit the various agents throughout the country. His journey was a series of explosions. The irritation engendered at the inefficiencies he found in one city was carried on to the next. Violent scenes were enacted. No excuses were accepted for poor business; as likely as not the agent was discharged summarily before he had had an opportunity to present his case. The old personnel were dropped in rapid succession and as rapidly replaced by men whose aggressiveness passed the requirements of the violent executive.

The agents whom he collected were active men, alert to advance their local business. They took a certain pride in the fact that they could hold their own under a fighting manager. The agents liked each other; they could appreciate the fact that there were few weaklings in their ranks. But in reality they did not like the sales manager, for they realized that he was often unfair and needlessly hot-tempered. Nevertheless, he became to them a sort of tradition, about which many stories grew and were repeated with gusto. He was a symbol of the

[165]

agents' efficiency, and therein lay their own regard for him—although they did not appreciate this fact. At the sales convention they collected a purse to buy a watch for the "chief" and presented it as a token of their "esteem and affection."

In the home office Lawrence was domineering and dominating. His explosions in the board-room were a matter of much comment. The president's lot was an unhappy one and at the first opportunity he resigned. Everyone, including Lawrence himself, seemed positive that he would be asked to take the president's place. But an outsider, an internationally recognized figure in the business, was selected.

When the announcement came to Lawrence, he was in the midst of his morning's work. He resigned instantly, but not peacefully. He threw his pen across the room, tore in half a report he was writing, and with a sweep of his arm brushed the papers from his desk. He crossed the main office in a blind rage—"damning" the directors at every step. He got drunk. He did not formally resign, but word came indirectly to the company that he had taken a position with a rival concern and was vowing to devote his life to busting the business which he had built up—"God damn 'em!"

The explosions to which Charles Kelly and Guy Lawrence gave free vent seem often beyond any control. In consequence the explosives take part in scenes which are of great embarrassment to their families and subsequently to themselves. Between outbursts they may, and often are, charming and kindly people. But they fly into a rage against the driver who crowds them in a parking space, against the usher at the theater, the waiter at the restaurant, and the neighbor next door. Often as not their rage inflates, then bursts and scatters like a soap bubble. With its passage they are left shame-faced and repentant. Many, in fact the majority of explosives, repent deeply of their violence. In earnest efforts to make amends they as often as not fly again into a rage at the clumsiness of their own efforts.

Some explosives can for a time control their outbursts when they would be too costly, but usually the storm does not die out quickly under the restraint. Often it is vented on a substitute. And wives and children are not uncommonly the substitutes.

Thus Emil Brown, after being ordered off the street for loitering, said nothing to the police officer, but hurried home and brutally beat his wife and children. His behavior is, in essence, no different from that of the young lawyer, John Kilday. During an unsuccessful case in court, one in which he was goaded by the attorney for the opposing side, he realized the breaking-point of his rage was near at hand and, knowing the detrimental consequences of a violent outburst before the judge, left abruptly and went home. At the door he was questioned pleasantly by his wife as to his reason for arriving so early. At once he began to curse and shout. He slammed some clothes into a bag, left the house, and the same day instituted proceedings for a divorce on the grounds of incompatibility.

The group of explosives described here have all been more or less unpleasant individuals. But such in reality is by no means always the case. Explosives are always men of vigor; their impulses are strong; any unpleasant trait of their temperament is exaggerated by their aggression. But frequently they have great depth of feeling. When thus warm they are charming and lovable people. If they have a high degree of intelligence and insight they may also develop an amazing control of their temperamental peculiarity.

Charles Kelly had no great degree of intelligence, as was shown by his career after leaving college; Guy Lawrence had no great depth of feeling, and neither did Emil Brown or John Kilday. But Mr. George

Knight, of whom we shall tell here, had both warmth and intelligence. He could control his explosiveness. The center for his control was in his diminutive wife, Emma. Beside his towering bulk she took on the proportions of a child, but a word in her quiet voice quelled his most violent explosions. She knew the symptoms of his impending outbursts, and she as well as he understood their cause.

His first explosion of the day invariably started at the breakfast table. The family ate together at seven-thirty; Mr. Knight insisted on it as a family custom. Invariably, too, one of the older children would be late. Mr. Knight's rumbled pleasant greeting would be checked at the door as his eye caught the vacant chair. His lips would be drawn together; his chair jerked from its place. And then in his wife's voice would come the words that seemed always to ring in his ears: "Now, George!" And he would splutter: "I know! I know, Emma! But it isn't right. It isn't right!" The newspaper held with clenched fists would hide his face; he would pretend not to notice the delinquent member of the family who slipped late into his chair. Finished with breakfast, Mr. Knight would rise and, in leaving the room, shape his course to pass behind the child on whom only a few moments before he had wished to vent his rage. But now there would be a clumsy pat upon the shoulder. It was his apology. He was as ashamed of himself as if he had roared and made a scene.

The children smiled at one another; they knew their father's ways. And the smile was born in deep affection.

At the office a dozen times a day the tension would build up in him to the bursting-point. His neck would stiffen, his clenched fist beat softly on the desk. And then, as if in reply to the familiar admonition of his wife, he would say: "I know! I know! But it isn't right!"

And then for a time he would ignore the clerk or stenographer who was responsible for his tension. An hour later he would on some excuse leave his office and, as if by chance, pass by the offender. Like a clumsy boy he would rest his hand for a moment on the clerk's shoulder. It was his apology for the threatened outburst. When he was gone, the clerks would smile at one another; they knew their employer's ways; but their smiles, too, were bred in deep affection. His staff were loyal to Mr. Knight; they had grown old in willing service to him.

Charles O'Day has the same warmth and the same explosiveness as Mr. Knight; but he lacks the intelligence to hold in check his outbursts. His control is of a different kind.

O'Day is employed as an information clerk in the railroad depot of a large city. A more trying position for an explosive would be difficult to find. But he has learned to hold back the tension aroused in him by the endless stupid questions that fill his working-day. His manner is one of studied courtesy. His is a painful forced patience.

Good jobs are scarce, and there are Mary and the youngster. The boy is five now and his father's pride. That is what makes his occasional outbursts hurt so much. The boy meets him at the door with shrill questions. There were nights when his explosiveness had reached the peak of endurance and he had struck the child. The expression on the tiny face tortured him. But the blow was struck; it could not be taken back nor yet forgotten in a flood of presents.

Today he prevents these scenes by an evasion. On those nights when he feels that the tension has reached the limit of his endurance he stops at the corner store and telephones his wife. She keeps the boy in the back of the house, out of the father's way, until with the comfort and relaxation of the evening meal the tension dies away.

[171]

The element of control and the direction given to the outbursts among explosives are matters of character formation. And, as would be expected, alcohol, by removing this restraint, has exposed many an otherwise controlled explosive. Often it makes him a fighting drunk, ready to quarrel on the slightest provocation.

Chapter V

BONDAGE IN MOODS AND EMOTIONS (*Continued*)

THE irritable is mildly explosive in temperament, but he differs from the true explosive in his fundamental mood and also in the intensity of his reactions. The explosive may be cheerful, highly congenial between explosions, but the irritable has continuously an unpleasant inner feeling, a mood of irritability. For him every situation in life presents annoyances to which he responds by immediate bursts of anger, not the cataclysmic rages of the explosive, but a series of petty angers, a series of "Why did you do that?" "What is the meaning of this?" He is the teaser and nagger and fault-finder. He fusses and fumes over trifles; magnifies minor faults into calamities. He habitually growls at those who err; he snarls at those who accidentally bump into him on the street. In traveling he finds continual sources of annoyance—the railroad, the boats, the food, the service, the beds. At home the annoyances are present equally; merely the sources are different—the telephone, the children, the neighbors, the radio. As a group the irritables have originated and perpetuated the familiar parental questions delivered with a snarl: "Can't you let me alone?" "Can't you see I'm busy?"

The irritables are usually unpleasant people, but they are to be pitied rather than condemned. They are far more unpleasant to themselves than they are to others. Their peculiar mood continually gives them a feeling of ill-being. Their fault lies in their lack of insight into their true condition. And there are sound reasons for this lack of self-understanding.

The normal man can be irritable if he is irritated sufficiently. He does not then feel comfortable, but his discomfort passes when the cause for his irritability is removed. Likewise the explosive may be free from his unpleasant inner tension between his outbursts. He then views the world in a pleasant light. A contrast is offered for comparison. But for the irritable there is no contrast; the world always appears unpleasant.

He has no way of judging himself or the world except by his own sensations. Consequently he attributes the cause of his unpleasant feeling entirely to his environment. The fault seems to him always on the outside and not on the inside. As a result, the irritable rarely feels the remorse of the explosive, or of the normal man who has been carried away by a passing feeling of irritability. A similar misinterpretation, giving rise to a testiness, is often seen in the aged. It has in part, at least, its origin in a failing memory for recent events. Articles are laid aside and their places forgotten; the newspaper, the slippers, the pipe, the spectacles are always being searched for and querulous complaints directed against the members of the household for moving them.

Irritability, like explosiveness, is often costly to its possessors, and is a handicap both in the business and social activities that is hardly compensated for by the aggressive vigor, the strong impulse so often associated with this type of temperament.

Such was the case with Dr. Heydey. He was admittedly the best diagnostician in a large Western city and had at one time an extensive consulting practice. As time went on his irritability increased with age. Patients referred to him by their physicians refused to see him. His reputation as an "impossible person" was spread quite as widely as his reputation as a consultant.

His office manners were described from personal experience by Mrs. Moffett, a lady of well-balanced personality who was amused rather than offended by his gruffness. She made the mistake, however, of trying to counteract his irritability by being overly gracious. When she entered his office, he ignored her amenities. His first remark to her was, "Well, what's the matter with you?" And before she had time to reply he entered upon a tirade about her probable diet, her high heels, her present mode of living, her cocktails, society women in general and their lack of occupation in particular. He concluded with: "What do you expect a doctor to do? Perform miracles? Take off your clothes."

As the nurse led the lady toward an anteroom his parting injunction was, "Strip, and don't be a prude about it."

During the moments in which the lady disrobed he delivered a monologue directed presumably at the nurse. It began with a preamble on the length of time women took to get off their clothes, and passed from that to styles and then on to the tomfoolery of women when the only important thing was to find out "what the hell was the matter with them." And since Mrs. Moffett was unhurried in her undressing and the nurse too inured to the doctor's manners to find any cause to hurry her, the tirade was extended to include over-eating, over-drinking, over-smoking—"Why don't they live as human beings are supposed to live, not like pampered dolls?

Why don't they get more exercise? Why don't they take care of themselves? Then they wouldn't need to be examined, and a busy man could have time for serious things."

The matter that irritates Dr. Heydey most of all is the one which he is quite incapable of understanding— why his practice is falling off.

If the irritable can obtain insight into their temperamental peculiarity, if they can be made to realize that the source of their unpleasant feeling lies within themselves and not in their environment, they may be able to develop control. Usually this fortunate insight is gained only after many costly experiences, sometimes tragedies.

It was a near tragedy that brought insight and control to Clara Nelmes. She had married Robert Ray, and he was an explosive. Both were strong and aggressive; they were intelligent and cultured. But Clara nagged Robert, and Robert exploded. They both vented their unpleasant feelings on their only child.

If Robert had been meek and mild, he might have endured the nagging and become a henpecked husband. If Clara had had insight, most of Robert's explosions could have been avoided. But as matters were, many were the scenes that grew from Clara's smoldering unpleasantness and Robert's volcanic outbursts.

A divorce on the grounds of incompatibility seemed the only solution. Clara kept the child. But Robert's modest salary gave insufficient alimony to support her and the boy. She decided to teach and secured a position in an elementary school. She had in high degree the intelligence, equipment and cultural training required for the position, but she was totally unsuited temperamentally.

Fortunately in the three months that intervened between her appointment and the opening of school she obtained at least a partial insight into her irritability. It came through trouble with her boy, Robert, Jr., then nine years of age.

Robert had inherited some of his mother's irritability and some of his father's explosiveness. He was a difficult child for anyone to handle; an impossible one for Clara. The scenes between her and the boy were repetitions of those that had occurred between her and her husband. She nagged the child; he sulked and then burst into storms of uncontrollable temper. She resented the similarity that the child showed to his father, and she puzzled over the fact that the boy failed to have the bright and cheerful periods between outbursts that

Robert had shown. The child was sullen and cross. His irritability kindled her own.

In preparation for the coming school term she engaged a maid, a Polish peasant girl of striking pyknic physique and of pleasant phlegmatic temperament. The maid and Robert, Jr., were soon on the friendliest terms. Clara resented the ease with which the girl handled the child; she was irritated at both.

The situation came to a climax one morning at the breakfast table. The child asked his mother to allow him to have an air rifle. Clara gave a snapping refusal. The boy sulked. She scolded him for his sulkiness. He left the table, and a moment later a crash of something falling brought her running into the back hall. The boy had taken a book from her desk on the second floor and thrown it down the backstairs. She darted for the child: "How dare you touch my books! I have forbidden you. How dare you!"

But the maid stood a stolid monument of flesh between the threatening Clara and the sullenly resentful child. The storm of Clara's irritability veered from the child to the maid. The girl listened unmoved until there was a momentary lull in the flow of bitter words. And then she said, calmly: "You're mean to him. You are a mean lady. The boy is just like you. He is cross. You make him cross."

Clara instantly discharged the maid. But the girl was unperturbed; she calmly finished her breakfast and washed the dishes before she began with slow deliberation to pack her belongings. The boy sulked in his room, muttering just loud enough for Clara to hear him in her room: "I want an air gun. I'm going to have an air gun."

In quick strides Clara walked back and forth across the floor, her hands alternately clenched and unclenched, her mind a prey to torment. Her pride, as well as her temperament, had been touched upon. A Polish peasant had called her mean. She made the boy cross, did she? The boy was just like her, was he? It was incredible! And yet was it? The dawning of insight is often painful. Clara suffered; but when she finally came from her room that morning she had a new determination and the beginning of a new outlook.

Today Clara is considered the least irritable and most patient of the teachers in her school. She has a calm—a studied, enforced calm that, if a little strained, is never broken. Clara, in gaining control, has lost temperamental judgment; she cannot now always trust her feelings. It is only the quivering of her flesh, the tremble of her mouth about her fixed smile, and a certain abruptness of manner that give clues to the strain under which at times she suffers. It is then that her voice grows even softer and her words are spoken even more slowly.

And in the home? Matters there are peaceful. The Polish maid is admirable. Robert, Jr., is actually friendly toward his mother. And that in spite of the fact that he did not get his air gun. He is saving his spending-money to pay for the book he ruined on a certain memorable day. Clara is determined that he shall learn early in life that temperamental outbursts may be costly. If the book is paid for without one single explosion of temper, then he may have the gun.

The true irritable does not seek out an antagonist against whom to relieve his unpleasant feeling. He discharges his irritability against the nearest person or the nearest object. But there is a special class of the irritables who seek out for the relief of their tension antagonists who will struggle against them. They are the quarrelsome who disagree with everyone, not in order to exploit themselves as does the egocentric, but for the sake of a heated argument.

The Phlegmatic.—The groups that we have presented here as the vivacious, the excitable, the explosive, and the irritable all have in common high emotional reac-

tions; the phlegmatics, on the contrary, are characterized by their temperamental inertia, their lack of emotion, their poverty of movement. The great inner
tension that develops in the readily excitable like a
hurricane is, in the phlegmatics, a mere zephyr. They
possess a calmness that can be shaken with difficulty;
they are stolid, undemonstrative men and women and
as such often a source of great irritation to their vivacious acquaintances.

Frequently they give the impression of dullness, but
theirs is not necessarily a poverty of thought, merely
an economy of thought. They are not troubled by a
flight of ideas, they are not distracted by a play of emotions; rather they follow one thought calmly through
to its logical and complete conclusion. They are a rock
against which the high-pressure salesman dashes his
emotion-stirring patter in vain. They are the ponderous
stabilizers of excitable and explosive committee members; neither threatened panic nor imminent prosperity
stirs them to sudden action. They are the great sitters
in club windows, the born *habitués* who can remain
for hours at the table calmly smoking and drinking,
and largely enjoying a joke told slowly and in minute
detail by an equally phlegmatic companion. Or they
can sit equally contentedly in silence.

Jonathan Humphrey was phlegmatic; his friends in derision called him "Speedy John." His slowness exasperated his wife. She vowed that he took years in getting ready to propose to her; in fact, she had to make him do it or he would still be calling on her and still be getting ready to propose. And he had never changed his slow ways in all the years of their married life; more than anything else he seemed to enjoy sitting in a comfortable chair, smoking his pipe, sometimes for hours not speaking a word. At times Mrs. Humphrey, who has her moments of mild vivacity, could scream at John's stolid calm. "Lord! If he'd only say something —do something. Even if he got into a scandal it would be better than always seeing him the same, day in and day out! If he'd only take some responsibility in raising the children instead of leaving everything for me!"

The children think he is a good father. He never becomes excited or scolds, no matter what they do. He never refuses his consent to anything they wish to do; he just tells them to ask mother. He never offers them advice, but he will sit and listen to them while they tell him of their difficulties and their arguments. He is patient and unselfish; he never seems to want anything for himself. If they forget one of his presents at Christmas—and it is almost a tradition that some one will—he never minds in the least; in fact, it isn't much use to give him a present, for he has not unwrapped several from years gone by.

When guests come to the house he rarely joins in the conversation unless asked a question, and then before he answers he ponders over it even if it is a trivial matter. He gives to each answer a certain ponderousness that passes with many people as an air of deep wisdom. He never argues about politics or anything else—he goes down each year and votes the Republican ticket. He always has.

The only sign of irritation he ever shows is when his daughter-in-law visits the home. She is vivacious and talks incessantly; she lisps. He leaves the house on the days she is there.

Most people consider John nice and kind; but many feel that he is indifferent to all civic matters. In fact, he came in for some sharp criticism both at home and at his club when the subscription was taken to buy stock in the new hotel. The town was seized in the throes of a boom, and all of the excitable inhabitants caught the contagion. The affair assumed the proportions of a patriotic appeal; new streets were laid out, real estate changed hands and prices thrice in twenty-four hours. Stock for the hotel was sold with a flourish of brass bands and church socials. Every wealthy citizen bought some—except John and one or two of his friends. He didn't see any reason for the excitement, and he wasn't disturbed when the boom collapsed. His money was well invested in bonds as solid and unmovable as he.

John has one particular crony who comes occasionally and sits with him. Sometimes they don't see each other for a month at a time, just when the spirit moves one of them. The two occasionally play Russian bank, pondering a long while over each move. The family does not like father's friend. He is a bore, and while he resembles father in many ways, particularly in his slowness, he is not as kindly or as patient. Often he gets angry at little things, is irritable and stubborn. He is very sensitive about a birthmark on his face; once he flew into a violent rage and nearly killed a man who teased him about it.

But father's most cherished friend is his daughter, the youngest of the three children. When they are together everyone smiles. Helena is a tiny duplicate of her father. Often the two sit together, her hand in his, for hours at a time without either saying a word.

John has one hobby. He is almost sentimental about his horses, and they seem to love him. He certainly understands them from every angle, and when he enters them in shows, he invariably gets a ribbon. The family exhibits the trophies as father's; but father always speaks of them as belonging to the horses.

Not all phlegmatic men have the comfortably cheerful mood and depth of resonance that Jonathan Humphrey exhibits. Some have moments of irritability or ill-humor; others will occasionally build up slowly a determined rage that bursts with unexpected and crushing violence and cools off as slowly as it rises.

The phlegmatic element of temperament appears in the personalities of many men in much less degree than in that of Jonathan Humphrey; they are more easily aroused; their fundamental lack of excitability shows merely in ponderousness, deliberation, and in poverty of movement and speech. The same lack in quickness of thought, in sparkling repartee, and in small talk, which often makes the intelligent phlegmatic appear dull, gives to others of lower intelligence an owl-like solemnity which is mistaken for a sign of wisdom.

And finally there are some phlegmatics who are even less excitable than Jonathan Humphrey. They are torpid. They are almost completely devoid of emotional reactivity. And they are completely unapproachable; no one can get in contact with their inner selves. They appear to have no pleasures and no sorrows. They may be intelligent; they may, if their family urges them, make their ponderous way through college.

A single incident from the life of a torpid college boy will serve to illustrate this sluggish temperament:

William Henry Draper was eating his dinner with vast deliberation at the college dining-hall. He was still slowly spooning his soup when one of his vivacious table mates had finished the meal. The active boy in a spirit of torment picked up a piece of toast and with the remark: "Here Bill, this will hurry you in getting rid of the soup," he threw the toast into Draper's plate. The soup was splashed across the boy's tie and vest and coat. Slowly he bent his head to look at the damage; as slowly he laid down his spoon and took up his napkin. He wiped his clothes carefully while the other boys waited for the expected outburst. But it didn't come. Finally he raised his head and drawled with no feeling whatever, "If you do that again I am apt to get mad."

He continued with the remains of his soup, and since the toast was still in the plate, he ate that also.

THE MOODS

The qualities of temperament dealt with so far have, except in the case of the irritable, concerned mainly degrees of excitability. Deliberately mood has been given a subordinate place. It is possible to do so because the display of a predominant mood is not a necessity of all temperaments; many personalities in regard to mood can be classified only as indifferent. There are, however, others in whom mood is the most striking feature of the entire temperament. So much so, in fact, that it colors indelibly the whole behavior of the individual and exerts a profound influence upon character formation.

Although mood and excitability are not directly related, there are nevertheless certain associations. Thus a gloomy mood rarely occurs in marked degree in the vivacious or excitable. Irritability, on the contrary, rarely occurs in the unexcitable. In fact, so close is it allied to excitability that we have included it in the previous section. Cheerfulness occurs more often in the readily excitable than in the phlegmatic. In either case its display is influenced by the degree of excitability; the phlegmatic may show a comfortable cheerfulness, a mild geniality, while the vivacious are prone to exhibit a militant optimism, an aggressive gaiety.

The Cheerful.—Cheerfulness affects character formation less perhaps than any other mood, except the indifferent one. It shows no striking peculiarities save in degree of resonance. The cheerful are often believed to be warm and sympathetic; far oftener they are quite the contrary. The cheerful have a pleasant inner feeling; it is the source of their cheerfulness. But it does not follow that this pleasant sensation is correspondingly extended into their regard of others, that they are necessarily approachable, congenial, and warm-hearted. In fact, they may be and often are decidedly superficial in their feelings. They tend to dismiss the trouble of their friends with a heartless gaiety. Sometimes they are totally incapable of appreciating the sorrows of others; and sometimes they deliberately flee from those with troubles and seek an environment better suited to the display of their elevated mood. On the other hand, cheerfulness is a pleasant mood in social surroundings; one joyous person, even of superficial feelings, acts like a leaven, raising the spirits of an entire group. An opposite effect, but to a less degree, is exercised by a gloomy person; an irritable one engenders uneasiness.

The Gloomy.—True gloomy individuals have, like the irritable, an unpleasant inner feeling. It is one of sadness. But usually they lack the inner tension, the excitability, and the aggression of the irritable. They are sad, subdued people, continually depressed. They see all life's experiences, both present and future, as dark. They are the inveterate pessimists. They expect the worst to happen and are not particularly disturbed when it does. As one gloomy individual expressed his outlook on life, "I always expect the worst and I'm generally right."

The pessimism of the gloomy stands in the way of flexible character formation. They overestimate all obstacles and all failures, often to such an extent that they find difficulty in following out any line of action. They are discouraged and defeated before they start.

Their skepticism, their sense of the futility of human effort, often makes the gloomy, scathing, penetrating critics such as was Edgar Allan Poe. In the nature of their criticism they differ markedly from the cheerful, who tend to praise with utter disregard of merit. They differ also from the egocentrics who criticize with self-inflation continually in mind. The destructive criticism of the egocentric belittles his competitors and so by contrast aggrandizes himself; his praise extols his dependents and so by association again aggrandizes him. The gloomy are dispassionate critics; they are not perverted by envy or carried away by enthusiasm. Instead they listen patiently for the sour note that they expect to hear, and they are rarely disappointed. Their praise

[190]

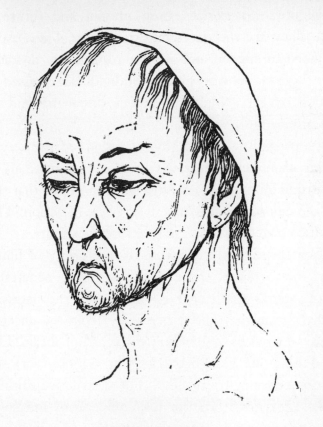

THE FEARFUL MAN
"He declares he has been affrighted by a certain dream."
*From the English translation of the "Characters"
of Theophrastus*

is not the extolling of goodness, but a surprised comment on the absence of badness.

There are indeed few situations from which the gloomy man fails to extract at least a drop of bitter. If a visitor admires his home, he is prone to pass off the praise with some such remark as: "Yes, I suppose it's all right, but about once a year there is a terrible odor from the rendering-plant." The rendering-plant is ten miles away. If the visitor comments favorably on the sunshine, the reply points out the inconveniences: the crops will dry up; the lawns will burn; it will be unbearably hot. If the comment is on the relief given by the rain, the reply in turn will point out equal inconveniences: the crops will be drowned out; the lawns will be flooded; the house will become damp; and his books will mildew.

The gloomy, in spite of their pessimism, often, but not always, have depth and warmth of feeling. Their sadness, their own sense of suffering, seem to make them particularly sensitive and compassionate to the suffering of others. This warm-heartedness of the gloomy frequently is hidden under a covering of cynicism. They are sincere and unostentatious in their acts of kindness, but they are dubious both of the benefits conferred and of the gratitude expressed.

[193]

Most of the gloomy are sluggish in movement; they are depressed, weighed down by the troubles of life. Often they attempt to hide their sadness and disguise it under an air of seriousness and ponderous thoughtfulness. Consequently it is far more difficult to recognize the mood of gloominess than that of cheerfulness. At times the deception can be detected in the posture and facial expression; the weary, drooping eyes, the mournful mouth with wrinkles that run to the nose, the drooping shoulders and the flickering one-sided smile that is an acknowledgment of a joke but not of any feeling of humor.

Not all the gloomy are at the extreme of the mood we have pictured here. Many men have merely a taint of gloominess in their temperament that lends a mildly drab color to their outlook on life. Again, some degree of gloominess may be mixed with a mood of irritability. The true gloomy is quiet and resigned; he lacks excitability; he is not aggressive or obnoxious in his unpleasant inner feeling. But an admixture of irritability gives a particularly unpleasant aggressive quality to the temperament. The result is sullenness and ill-humor as seen in the typical "grouch," the crabbed man who is content neither with himself nor with the world, and who expresses his dissatisfaction unstintingly.

The Anxious.—Anxiety is the basis of more varied modes of behavior than any other of the moods. Not only does it give a peculiar coloration to all of the ordinary activities of the individual, but it is a source from which spring actual phobias and devious physical symptoms resembling those of disease. The anxious are legion; from their ranks come many of the psychoneurotics.

Transient moods of anxiety are familiar to nearly everyone. They arise from a sense of insecurity. No men are so fortunately placed as to be beyond all threat from their environment; few men are so invulnerable as to fail to sense at times the threat. All experience anxiety. Today a sense of economic insecurity is perhaps the most widespread; the next is insecurity against disease. There are sound reasons for the anxieties of the normal man; but when the source of danger is for a time removed, his anxieties are relieved. But such is not the case for those of anxious temperament. The source of their anxiety lies within them. Anxiety is their fundamental mood. The anxious are filled with a tension of expectancy, a sense of foreboding, a feeling of apprehension.

A normal man when suffering from a spell of anxiety may show physical signs of his distress; he may be restless, sleepless; and if his anxiety is acute he may pale and tremble; his bodily functions may become deranged and he may suffer from indigestion, palpitation of his heart, and headache. When troubled by anxiety, the normal man knows the cause and he attempts to find relief by bettering his insecure position. His efforts for security show in his behavior.

The man of anxious temperament exhibits these same characteristics, but in greatly heightened degree; he shows them without the real provocation that is needed to call them forth in the normal man. He shows them in some degree in all his actions.

The slightest threat to his security throws him into a panic of apprehension; the slightest responsibility fills him with fear. After a decision is made he suffers in the anxiety that he has made the wrong one. The fear of indecision may occupy his mind to such an extent that his obligations in other directions are unfulfilled. A chance remark is for him replete with menace. Thus when the insurance doctor asks him as a matter of routine if any of his ancestors have had cancer, his anxiety causes him to read a false meaning into the words: the doctor is hinting that it is he who has cancer. He worries about cancer.

The anxious man is always living in the future; he wakes up in the morning with the question, "What will happen to me today?" And he goes to bed with the question: "What will happen to me tomorrow?" He can't enjoy the theater because he is thinking constantly of how soon the entertainment will end. When his wife is ill, he becomes so anxious that he wakes her out of a sound sleep to ask her if she is feeling better.

The anxious man crosses all his bridges before he comes to them. On a motor trip he asks the road directions from every tourist he meets and every traffic officer he sees and at every filling station at which he stops. And the stops are many, for he fears that he will run out of gasoline or that the oil is low. In between stops he studies his road maps and asks innumerable questions about the hotels, the weather, and the state of the pavement. He needs continual reassurance, and the reassurance fails to reassure him.

The anxious man, if he is inclined to be vivacious, shows a peculiar form of restlessness; often it takes the form of being ahead of time for all engagements.

Thus Harold O'Dell was filled with the restlessness that arose from a vague anxiety. And his anxiety was keenest when there was an appointment to be kept. He was always ahead of time; in the fear of being late he sacrificed his own time without stint. He always arrived at dinner parties embarrassingly early and then only after he had walked by the house a dozen times, counting the minutes on his watch. He was half an hour early in awaiting the arrival of a train, and that in spite of the fact that he had purchased his tickets a week before and checked his baggage a day early. The half-hour wait was spent in a panic of restlessness that forced him to walk about, disregarding the tasks at hand. He was brusque, almost impolite, to those who accompanied him. He was engaged in a multitude of unnecessary activities. He felt continually to see if his tickets were in his pocket, if his purse was in place. He counted and recounted the baggage. He checked his watch against the station's clock to reassure himself of the train time, appeared to forget it at once and sought assurance again.

The search for constant security to which their mood directs them often makes the anxious take elaborate and useless precautions against all possibilities. For even a brief trip they may carry a great assortment of unnecessary impedimenta; the rubbers, the umbrella, the raincoat, and the first-aid kit, are much in evidence; identification cards are carefully filled out in their purses. On the trip or at home they avoid draughts and avoid getting their feet wet; they are meticulously careful of their food and drink. They are the patent-medicine dealers' best customers, the faddists' best clients, the insurance man's most vulnerable prospects.

Their anxiety embraces all the members of their family. Their children must carry their rubbers to school if there is a cloud in the sky, and wear an extra sweater if a breeze is blowing. They live in a continual terror of some one in the family being injured.

There was a certain Mrs. Poultney who thus regulated her whole life in the interest of security—security against her own inner tension of anxiety. She admitted that she always expected something to happen, but she couldn't define exactly what it was—"just everything." When first married, her husband wanted her to live in the suburbs and drive to the city, but she wouldn't consider the idea for a moment; she had a thousand reasons against it. She chose instead an apartment in a rather poor part of town. She chose it because a firehouse was only two blocks away, a police station at the corner, and the hospital no more than a minute's walk. Her husband humored her; he even helped her attach the safety locks she had purchased for the windows and doors. But he soon learned that it was useless to try to reassure her, for as soon as he argued her fears down on one thing, she found other causes for anxiety.

His suggestion that all that was needed to make the

neighborhood complete was a mortuary parlor, brought to her mind Aunt Minnie. She suddenly felt that Aunt Minnie was dying and the conviction grew so strong that she telephoned to her in Chicago, eight hundred miles away. Aunt Minnie, so it happened, was enjoying especially good health at the moment. But telephoning was one of Mrs. Poultney's failings. She called all her friends and acquaintances if she had not seen them for a day or two, just to ask them how they were.

Aunt Minnie had heart disease, and periodically over a span of ten years Mrs. Poultney had predicted her death. The final prediction was within a week of the fatal date, whereupon, like all prophets, she forgot her bad guesses and remembered only her one successful one. She had, so she said, "a feeling when something dreadful was going to happen—a premonition." Sometimes she woke up in the middle of the night with one of her "premonitions," but it was thunderstorms especially that threw her into a flurry of dire predictions. After the storm was over she made many telephone calls.

Twice each day, at nine and three, she suffered an especial apprehension. At these hours the mail was left at the house. To open a letter was a dread, a telegram a fright, and a toll call a horror of uncertainty until the connection was completed.

In fact, every new experience was a cause of suffering. For years the family had been spending the time of Mr. Poultney's vacation at a mountain resort. As the years went by the resort became shabby; the old visitors left and were replaced by a class that made the Poultneys uncomfortable. The children wanted to try a new resort, but mother didn't want to change, she was so used to the old place.

Some of the anxious suffer acutely from the physical signs that may accompany their unfortunate mood. Often the most annoying is what they call dizziness, but which in reality gives the sensations of swaying, sinking, and floating, rather than the sensation that the surroundings are moving about them. Dryness of the mouth, shortness of breath, palpitation of the heart, nausea, belching, heartburn, abdominal pains, and even vomiting may arise from the tension of anxiety, as may also such minor manifestations as sweating, flushing, trembling. But the most distressing feature that can occur is the panic of apprehension that makes the anxious feel that they are about to faint, go mad, or die. Some of the anxious never suffer from such acute attacks;

others have them only to a mild degree, and still others suffer from them acutely.

Not infrequently a physician is hastily called at night to treat one of these attacks of acute anxiety. He finds the members of the family in great distress, for the patient appears to be in a serious condition. He is in bed or occasionally staggering frantically about his room. His expression is one of extreme fear. His hands are clammy, his limbs trembling. His heart beats violently, so violently, in fact, that the bed may shake. Often the patient's abdomen is distended with gas. His breaths are in short gasps; he is overcome with a sense of suffocation. If it is a true anxiety attack the physician finds nothing physically wrong with the patient.

But it is difficult, almost impossible, to convince the patient that his palpitating heart, his sense of suffocation, and his apprehension of death arise solely from his peculiar temperamental mood of anxiety. Rather he is convinced that the situation is entirely the opposite, that his anxiety arises from some serious physical disturbance in his heart, his lungs, or his digestive system. His anxieties focus on what he believes to be his disease. He becomes then a typical psychoneurotic, suffering from what the physician often calls a cardiac, or respiratory, or gastric neurosis.

No ordinary form of treatment intended to correct disordered organic function will relieve the condition. The treatment to be effective must attack the seat of the trouble, the anxiety of the patient. Either his confidence in recovery must be gained to such an extent that he believes he is cured (treatment by suggestion which has a fine foundation in psychotherapy, but which is also widely exploited by charlatans) or else, if he is intelligent, he may be relieved by an explanation that gives him a true insight into the cause of his disturbance.

The medical profession is learning rapidly that it is worse than useless merely to say to such patients, "There is nothing the matter with you except your imagination." The patient knows better; he can feel that something is the matter. His reaction to this statement is the natural one: if this doctor does not know what is the matter with him, another does. He will try another one, and another, and still another, and probably a few fads as well, and a charlatan or two for good measure.

It is true, of course, that many of the anxious are not desirous of losing their "neuroses." They may complain bitterly of their symptoms, incessantly seek medical advice and purchase patent medicines, but their ailments none the less have a value to them. The value lies in the fact that their illness brings them sympathy and consideration. Sympathy and consideration in turn yield a modicum of security and freedom from responsibility. All these things the anxious desire.

But for the intelligent man of anxious temperament insight into his condition gives the only true security. With insight he can control the manifestations of his mood. He can say to himself, in effect: "The cause for this sensation of anxiety that torments me, lies within me. I am not threatened. I have no real cause for anxiety." Such brave regard of his condition will not rid him of the feeling of anxiety, but it will prevent him from seeking frantically, but in the wrong direction, for the cause of his anxiety. He will know that the palpitations of his heart, the sinking feeling in the pit of his stomach, and his "dizziness" are not the cause but the effect of his own fundamental mood. Knowing this fact, he will not then attribute his sensations to some serious disturbances, the mere thought of which drives him on to a panic of anxiety. Many of the anxious can and do control themselves. They learn in time to stand off from themselves as dispassionate observers and study their own mood; they learn to discount their own sensations.

But most of the anxious fail to gain this saving insight. Many, failing to do so, become psychoneurotics.

Some of these psychoneurotics succeed in rationalizing their anxiety. Most of them quite logically center their sensations about an acceptable physical cause. But there are others of the anxious mood whose rationalization is far less obvious to others, but nevertheless logical to them. They center their anxieties about some act or situation. They develop phobias.

All anxious individuals experience the sensation of uncertainty; they seek for an explanation of this sensation; they often refer it to some act they have recently performed. Thus there continually comes to their minds such questions as these: Did I turn off the water? Did I put out the lights? Did I mail the letter without stamps? Did I mail it at all? The anxiety that gives rise to the question is not relieved until they are literally compelled, against their will and against their better judgment, to return and see if they have shut off the water, put out the lights, or mailed the letter.

Often the reference of anxiety is to situations far more complex than those arising from the mere feeling that some simple act has been omitted. The entire anxiety is built into a highly complicated aspect of character formation; it appears symbolically. Such elaborate rationalizations of anxiety are called phobias.

Thus an anxious individual concerned for his health

may develop an exaggerated and unreasonable fear of germs. His whole behavior centers around his phobia. It becomes nearly impossible for him to shake hands, but if he is forced to do so, he immediately washes them. He sits in the last row of the theater so that no one will sneeze or cough on him; he avoids all public conveyances; he refuses to eat in restaurants or drink at bars or soda fountains; he hesitates to touch door knobs; he has his table dishes boiled. One such individual in our experience used an entire cake of soap each time he bathed; first he had to wash the soap itself vigorously to remove a contaminated layer; and then between washing each part of his body he washed the soap. He used six or more towels to dry himself. His elaborate and quite useless precautions against "germs" kept his anxiety largely centered in one area. His ritualistic acts gave him a sense of security. His curtailed activities kept him from many public and social situations that might have caused him anxiety.

The ritual of the phobia appears almost superstitious; unquestionably many of the superstitious who tap wood, throw salt over their shoulders, and the like, are fundamentally anxious in mood.

Many phobias are far more complicated in their content than the simple one of fearing germs; but many of even the most highly symbolic have in their limitation of the scope of activities a real as well as a symbolic value to their possessors. An anxious man whose phobia lies in the inability to go more than six blocks from his house retains—no matter what the elaborate symbolism of his phobia may be—a very limited environment and one that causes him the least distress and responsibility.

In short, the phobia, for all the complexity of character formation which gives it direction, is based on anxiety; it assists in some way—though the way may be devious—in obtaining the one thing that the anxious seek beyond all else—security.

The anxious as a group show no special reaction to alcohol, coffee, or tobacco. The tempo of their individual temperaments, as well as their fundamental mood, plays a part in the responses. But coffee in excess usually aggravates anxiety and insomnia; the same is true of tobacco. Alcohol, on the contrary, often gives great relief to the anxious during the initial stages of its action; but anxiety is increased correspondingly during the phase of returning sobriety.

The sexual relations of the anxious often play a prominent part in aggravating the mood; and conversely the mood itself often interferes with their sexual relations. In anxious women a common cause of acute attacks of anxiety lies in incomplete gratification during sexual intercourse. The practice of *coitus interruptus* as a contraceptive measure has frequently a definite deleterious effect upon the anxious of both sexes; it is often the direct exciting cause of the anxiety crises.

In the male the anxious mood often interferes with satisfactory sexual relations; the fear of impregnation, of premature ejaculation, of impotency, gives rise to so severe a sense of anxiety that normal sexual relations become impossible. The very mood itself may be a cause of impotency.

The Moody.—The relationship between mood-swings and the pyknic physique has been touched upon in Chapter II.

Fluctuations from one mood to another are within limits a regular part of all temperaments; but there are some in which the fluctuations are so extreme and so regular that they in themselves constitute the most striking features of the temperament. Such temperaments are called moody. There are men who regularly wake in the morning gloomy, taciturn, and morose, but who during the course of the day become quite cheerful, and by evening are pleasant, sociable, and even vivacious.

These changes in the temperament of the moody are quite different in nature from the transient depressions of the normally vivacious. The entire temperament alters. The vivacious man "down in the dumps" can be cheered up, livened up, and brought out of his "fit," but not so the true moody. In fact, they are annoyed and depressed still more by the well-meant efforts of their family and their friends to "cheer them up." They respond to this annoyance by becoming only more irritated or more taciturn. The strange moodiness that possesses them at times runs its period and passes away, and they are better if left alone in their depression. Often, however, their depression is greatly aggravated by hunger. A sandwich and a glass of milk, or a cup of tea or coffee, may restore in part their normal cheerfulness.

Terrence Warren had moods of this kind, but in his case they were moods covering long periods. There were months on end when he burst with activity, almost with gaiety, when there was a spring to his step and vigor to his voice, and when his laugh was quick and infectious. During the happy periods he had a multitude of interests: his friends, his dinners, his golf and tennis. His vigor was the envy of the men in the club where he lived; there were some whom he irritated but no one could bear a grievance against him long for his cheerfulness was warm and kindly. Never did he speak a word of bitterness or sarcasm, never could he intentionally hurt anyone. It was his morning bath that annoyed some of the less buoyant club members for he was a noisy bather. At seven-thirty his door crashed with a bang, the shower spluttered its fullest and his towel slapped and banged in time to a raucous and tuneless song. At eight-ten he passed the elevator and took his morning "constitutional" in a dash down the stairs to the dining-room.

Then would come a morning when the door did not slam, when the shower merely dribbled, when the towel was pushed slowly, almost mechanically, over his round body, and when the morning song did not echo through the halls. That day he took the elevator to the dining-room. To the cheery greetings of the head waiter he merely nodded. His smile had vanished, his face drooped in gloom, and his vivacity had given place to a sort of tense phlegmatism. Every movement was slow and difficult, as though he were lifting great weights at each step. His depression, his uneasiness, spread to everyone about him—there was a tenseness in the dining-room, an uncomfortable feeling.

Terrence Warren did not have insight into the cause of his changing moods. And his, perhaps, were too severe to be wholly discounted by the knowledge that the change was within him and not in the world about him. But for many individuals with minor mood-swings insight brings great comfort. It also greatly simplifies their relation with their friends and associates.

If a man who is dizzy from whirling about were actually to believe what his senses tell him, he would think that the ground was moving under his feet. He would argue and insist that he was stationary but that the surroundings were moving. His sensations told him that they were moving; he saw and felt the movement. But if he had insight that the perception of movement is a sensory deception, that the ground was stationary, and that he only thought it was moving, then he could discount his sensations.

It is insight into temperament that we have emphasized in this chapter. No man can ever change the nature of his temperamental endowment. If he is born viva-cious or phlegmatic, cheerful or irritable, anxious or moody, so he will remain. But he can learn to understand his temperament and to discount its peculiarities. When he has this insight, he has come closer to knowing the actualities of the world. Indeed, he has come close to knowing himself.

PART V

THE MEEK, THE MILD, THE MILITANT

Chapter VI

THE MEEK, THE MILD, THE MILITANT

I T IS from ego that springs all human self-esteem. In ego lies the source of man's noblest ambitions, and in it, too, all earthly vanities. Out of ego come the keenest satisfactions of life, and from it grow the most pathetic vagaries of human behavior. It is ego that raises strong men to the highest places of power; it is ego that brings weak men underfoot.

Ego is I—I in distinction to you.

Ego is for each man the consciousness of his own estimate of himself in relation to his own estimates of others. It involves the comparison of himself with his human environment. It is in this environment that his impulses must largely seek their goals. Hence to every man the environment is a threat of power that will oppose and thwart his efforts to obtain his personal satisfactions. If he is to express his own individuality, he must overcome this force. His strength is pitted against the opposition of the environment. Accordingly, he sets

[215]

a value on his own strength and he sets a value on the strength of his environment. The higher he estimates his strength, the lower he estimates the threat of his environment; and contrariwise, the lower he estimates his strength, the higher he estimates the threat environment. In either case his estimation determines the value he places on his ego. ·

In evaluating his ego the man does not wait until his life's work is done so that he can look back over his achievements and, in judgment, say: "I am strong or I am weak in comparison with other men; my strength or my weakness has been proved." Instead, even before he has tried his strength he sets the values. From infancy man senses his own strength or weakness. From this feeling, he sets his values and maintains them regardless of success or failure. Strength and weakness of ego are inborn.

The strength of ego is derived from the strength of the basic biological impulses that drive men on to seek their satisfactions in their environments. There are men with strong impulses in their personalities, and men with weak; correspondingly there are men with strong egos and weak egos. But always self-regard, weak or strong, is experienced by the man only through the qualities of his individual temperament and regarded through the qualities of his individual intelligence. Therefore, all strong egos and all weak egos are not experienced precisely alike by their possessors, nor are they manifest precisely alike to the world. A man with a strong ego, but with no mood of anxiety and with no warmth, experiences and manifests his ego strength in quite a different manner from a man with a strong ego but with mild anxiety, and some degree of warmth. The one would be an utterly cold and ruthless egoist; the other might be merely an egocentric or he might be a normal man.

The qualities of temperament, the degree of intelligence, and the strength of impulses are inborn. The display of intelligence and the strength of impulses vary with the phases of development. The strength of ego varies with these changes. The impulse life alters in strength as the individual passes from infancy to adolescence, from adolescence to maturity, and from maturity to senescence. With the changes the ego valuation varies, but the alteration is one only of degree. The young egoist does not become the meek soul in adult years, nor does the timid child become the egoist in after-life. The egoist may grow more egoistical or less; and the timid may gain some bravery. Likewise, the child who is egocentric during adolescence—and in adolescence all children have ego disturbances—may become reasonably normal when the stormy period has passed. But the fact remains that from the inherent qualities of personality the egoist is born to be an egoist; the egocentric an egocentric; the weak the weak. And such they will remain. There is nothing that can be done except to curb, or encourage, or discount, as the case may be, the manifestations of ego.

Intelligence and character formation exert their influences in shaping these manifestations; they at least relieve the more blatant crudities. The egoistical brat who pirates his mates of their toys learns in later life to be more subtle in his business piracies. The egocentric youngster who shows off to attract attention, as an adult talks about his ancestors, criticizes his friends, becomes a snob, or finds some equally acceptable way of exploiting his peculiarities. The timid child who runs screaming to his mother at every affront finds other "mothers" in the world to give him a more dignified shelter, or perhaps he may even put on a false face of fierceness to frighten others into leaving him alone even though he quakes behind it. But such superficial subtleties, such changes, such disguises, do not alter the underlying values or peculiarities of the ego. And it is these values that set the life regard in which each man views himself and his environment. It is they that establish the values of the goals for which each man strives. It is they that establish the fundamental nature of his relationship with his fellow men.

The man of normal ego, or nearly normal—for few are perfectly balanced in this quality of their personality—has a reasonably correct evaluation of himself and of his environment. The goals he sets in life are in accord with his values; they may be high or they may be low, but in either case they coincide with his true capacities to attain them. His ambitions are in proportion to his capability. And furthermore, his goals are productive ones. The satisfaction of his ego—the proving of self-esteem—comes primarily from accomplishment. But the importance of the accomplishments that bring satisfaction are not to be judged against the full scale of human endeavor, but against the scale of each man's individual capabilities.

A normal man of low capability obtains as much satisfaction from his inferior accomplishments as does a man of high capability from his superior ones. The child who builds a crude bird-house, the laborer who digs a hole in the ground, the artisan who makes an automobile, and the explorer who discovers a new island, may each experience the same degree of satisfaction from their accomplishments. Each, if he has a normal ego, can say, "I have done a good job." The normal child does not critically compare his bird-house unfavorably with one made by an artisan and say, "Mine is not much good." Rather he says, "Mine is as good as, or even better than, other boys my age can make." He feels no envy of the artisan, but rather he derives from his work a stimulus for further achievement—a higher goal. He will make better bird-houses when his capabilities are greater. Likewise the explorer who has discovered an island does not say, "My achievement is as nothing; Columbus discovered a whole continent." Neither does he say, "My discovery is everything; it far exceeds the accomplishment of anyone else." Rather he says, "In view of the difficulties that I have encountered I have done a good job and I have a right to a reasonable pride in it."

In any case, the boy, the laborer, the artisan, or the explorer, if he receives praise and prestige, his satisfaction in his accomplishment is increased. But on the other hand, it is equally a mark of his normal ego that if he does not feel that his accomplishment justifies the abundant praise he receives, he cannot from this prestige alone obtain the satisfaction of his ego. Prestige for him cannot be a substitute for accomplishment. His goals are valid ones.

Few normal men make an absolutely accurate estimate of their values in life; most have their conceits and envies, and ego weaknesses that influence their behavior. But there are some men who have them to such high degree as to cease entirely to be within the range of normal; the ego qualities of their personalities are markedly deviated. Their whole behavior is dominated by their ego peculiarities. Such men of necessity find far greater difficulty in adjusting to the common environments of civilization than do men who are more nearly normal. The environment of civilization is designed primarily to suit the average man; there are few positions in it which will allow the extreme egoist to fulfill his demands for absolute power, or the egocentric to obtain the boundless prestige he craves, or still to relieve the man of weak ego of all insecurity and fear. In any environment all men must give as well as take.

The development of civilization throughout its entire history has been in the direction of communal protection against the environment. And under this protection the man of reasonably normal ego can take his place with self-respect. He respects the achievements of others. He gives toward the support of his protective environment and he accepts in turn such shelter as it gives him. Such a man tends to identify himself with the institutions which represent the communal interests; he makes himself a part of the environment. He thinks and speaks of the country in which he lives as "my country," the place where he is employed as "my factory" or "my office," and so on down through the list of things that touch upon his life—"my children," "my wife," "my town," "my home," "my church," "my lodge," "my bank," "my doctor."

The use of the possessive is not in the aggressive sense of actual possession; in fact, he feels no sense of possession, but rather one of respect and identification. The broad institutions of his environment are vantage-points of security that he has justly earned, in which he has a right to participate and toward the support of which he has given his aid. He will criticize them if they do not fulfill his expectations; he will defend them if they are attacked.

The egoist cannot accept these institutions; he sweeps them aside as of no value to him except as stepping-stones to power. The egocentric finds them distasteful, for they demand achievement before prestige will be given. The man of weak ego finds them insufficient to give him the full and constant protection that he craves.

But the man of well-balanced ego usually accepts them with little critical scrutiny; they exist, they have always existed as far as he is concerned. They are to be accepted, not in resignation, but as a regular and normal part of life. Such a man is not a reformer, but neither is he without his self-respect. He accepts marriage and the raising of children and the paying of taxes without questioning the fundamental soundness of such institutions and without revolting seriously against the burdens they impose. But in accepting them he also stands up for what he has learned to believe are his personal rights; he insists on choosing his partner in matrimony; he is determined that his children shall be his own; and he demands a vote in the matter of taxation. In short, he accepts and supports with common sense the mores of his time.

The greater the threat from the environment the more firmly he embraces and participates in the institutions of communal protection and the sterner the fiber of these institutions becomes. A threat of danger drives his personal interests to the background. When an army is at the gate of the city, as one of the citizenry he is ready to accept the absolute domination of martial law; he is willing to subordinate himself for the common interest. When the crisis passes he demands and takes again his normal liberty.

In the past the threat of the environment was far greater than in the civilization of today. Consequently monarchs and tyrants throve as did a church militant. The spread of democracy and the rise of religious liberty, indeed the emancipation of the common man from virtual enslavement, owe their inception not to philosophical doctrines and fundamental principles, but to the fact that with the passage of time the world has become a less dangerous place in which to live. The threat of the environment has diminished and consequently the average man has been able to exercise his individual ego interests with a greater and greater degree of freedom. He has built institutions which are less rigorous than those of the past, but in which he has a far greater personal participation.

The environment in civilization is a common environment to the extent of the general institutions such as government, laws, and customs. But such things, while they touch the broadest aspects of each man's existence —the protection of life and liberty, justice before the law, and freedom of worship—are usually not matters of pressing interest to the average man. He has no difficulty in adjusting himself to their requirements. But such common institutions do not and cannot extend to the situation that concerns him only personally in his competition with his fellow men within the common environment. No communal institutions can give him assurance that he will succeed in life, that he will marry the woman he desires, or that if he does she will respect the marriage vows, that his children will live, that he will not lose his property or his employment, that disease will not affect him, and so on down to such things as failure of social acceptance and failure in school and college. These matters, insignificant as they may appear in contrast to the fundamental ones of the communal security given by institutions, are nevertheless vitally important in the life of each individual. They are, within their narrow range, constant threats from the immediate environment; they are constant challenges to self-esteem.

In response to these challenges men may show widely different reactions. Some react as minor egoists, some as egocentrics, and some show signs of ego weakness. Their behavior is influenced by their reaction; and in turn, from their behavior the characteristics of their ego can be recognized.

THE STRONG EGOS

The Egoist.—The life goal of the egoist is power—power for the sake of power. He feels superior to his environment; he does not fear its threat; he does not warm in sympathy to the needs of other men. As in all ego manifestations, temperament here plays a part. The egoist is cold. He is indifferent to the opinions of others; he disregards their criticisms and he asks no praise for his virtues. He wants none. He wants only power and he cares not how he gets it. His demand is for independence. He will not be restrained by the social responsibilities and conventions that hold other men. He is a world unto himself. He is an egoist.

From such stock in its extreme form come great leaders, great fighting pioneers, great tyrants, and great criminals. The aggressive leader must not be gentle or warm-hearted. He must step over others who seek the same goals that he seeks; he must step on others who can serve as a rung in the ladder to his power. Only an egoist can possess this hardness of personality.

The criminal egoist is a man at war with all society and contemptuous of his adversary. Many pirates and buccaneers have been egoists; some criminals in modern society are egoists. Such criminals often lack in intelligence; they may be stupid and miserable, but they do not lack in coldness and in ego overvaluation. They are the born criminals, constitutionally incapable of reform, to whom the jurist applies the term "morally insane." They cannot tell the ethical difference between right and wrong. It lies beyond their comprehension, for does not their ego tell them that their desires and their demands are always right? It is from such criminals that come the most appallingly heartless atrocities.

Again, a minor but brutal egoism appears in the torturing of animals—the adolescent who finds a pleasure in pulling the wings off flies, the man who dispassionately beats his sick horse, and the lady who goes away for the season without making provision for the care of her cat. But in regard to the treatment of animals it must be recalled that the concept of kindness to brutes is a very recent acquisition to society. A hundred years ago, such were the mores of our country and such are still the mores of some others, that the suffering of an animal was looked upon with no unpleasant regard by the average individual, particularly if the spirit of competitive sport entered into the situation. The Spanish who admire bull-fighting are no more a nation of egoists than were our Colonial ancestors who delighted in bear baiting.

All true egoists are by no means buccaneers, criminals, and animal torturers. In some circles many are highly admired and envied citizens. Thus there is the business man who ruthlessly wrecks his competitor; he is often an egoist, but the doors of society are not shut to him so long as his methods are within the law. And there is the man who discards his wife for the sake of financial or social betterment in a second marriage. Egoists also are those collectors of rarities who, by any means fair or foul, accumulate their treasures and obtain their satisfaction not by displaying their hoard to others, but merely from the feeling of power given by possession. Such men are not misers, for misers may be weak in ego, collecting their gold pieces for no sense of power, but only for a sense of security.

An egoist cannot be an underling, even though his intellectual capacities doom him to that rank, without a feeling of revolt. Neither can he show devotion to anyone or anything except his own ego. In the office and in the factory he is stubborn to those above him, cruel to those who compete with him, and indifferent to those below him unless they have something he desires. If they have he takes it without compunction or remorse, and makes no reparation. To him women are often a mere convenience for his desires. Love with devotion, self-sacrifice, are beyond the comprehension of the true egoist.

In the school the young egoist is uneducatable except as he wishes to be educated. If he is intelligent, education may be a stepping-stone in his search for power. If he is stupid, he is stubborn and defiant; often he demands his independence, and failing to achieve it peacefully, revolts and runs away.

The attitude of the egoist is not asocial so much as anti-social. Yet the egoist may be of great value to society. If his goal of power coincides with some interest of the community, the community may be benefited by his efforts. When his goal is political power, he may under some circumstances be an oppressive tyrant, and under others a useful aggressive leader of his country, expanding its borders and subduing its enemies. Cesare Borgia was such a leader. And egoists also are all followers of the doctrines that Machiavelli based on Borgia's strategies. Again, when the goal to power of the intelligent egoist is financial, he may be an aggressive capitalist who develops the resources of a country. The general population may derive benefits from his efforts, but these to him are purely incidental and indifferent aspects.

Needless to say, egoists in all walks of life are often highly successful individuals. The spoils of life are to the brave; and the egoist, although he may not be a physical hero, has social bravery. He has contempt for others; he has self-confidence; he has self-assurance; and, perhaps most important for his success, he has coldness. In his coldness he is devoid of the sympathies that make men "soft."

All of these qualities are valuable for those who, within a competitive society, seek power in business, professional or social life. And if the coldness of the egoist is repulsive, his very strength demands a grudging admiration. Here is a man who can stand on his own feet.

In dealing with the egoist we have stressed extreme qualities rather than the minor ones that occur in the personality of men who are within the range of normal. But unmistakably these qualities can be recognized in the inherent and wholly unconscious selfishness of many of our associates and particularly of some of our social and business and political superiors.

By preference the egoist plays a lone hand; he does not feel the need of support nor does he feel the need of human companionship; he rarely feels lonesome. But it must be borne in mind that the egoist can, when it is to his advantage, play a part and disguise his egoistical purposes. He prefers to dominate by fear, but if he cannot gain power by blunt aggression he may, if he is intelligent, win it by suave diplomacy. It is the end and not the means that is his primary interest. He will, if need be, accept, even enlist, the help of others to attain his objective, but with this certain eventuality: when the objective is gained and assistance no longer needed, his helpers will be cast aside unrecompensed even in gratitude.

And finally, popular opinion to the contrary, the egoist is never a braggart. His exploits are in deeds, not words. If he seeks publicity, it is because publicity has a value other than of flattery, a value that advances his quest for power. The braggart is the egocentric. And in the egocentric we come to a quality found far oftener in the personality of the average man than true egoism.

The Egocentric.—The life goal of the egocentric is prestige—prestige for the sake of prestige. The egocentric, like the egoist, has a strong ego, but unlike the egoist it is colored with a vague sense of anxiety and uncertainty. He feels that he is strong, but at the same time his strength is not self-sufficient. He needs continual assurance of his superiority to his environment. The proof, and only proof, that gives him this assurance is prestige.

All men except the extremely egoistical and the extremely weak want prestige, but the well-balanced man appreciates it only when it is truly deserved. He wants first and foremost the satisfaction of accomplishment; prestige increases his satisfaction, but in all endeavors it is not his primary aim.

The normal man and the egocentric face quite differently the problems of self-advancement. To the well-balanced man the urge of ambition resolves itself into such questions as these: How can I better myself and extend the scope of my activities? How can I obtain a better position in my work and obtain with it a greater economic and social security? How can I win the means to help my wife and children, the means by which the family will be relieved of hardship and assured of comforts and pleasures?

For the egocentric the corresponding questions are: How can I build myself up so that I shall seem superior to other men? How can I make them admire me and be envious of me and jealous? How can I hold back other men so that I can retain my prestige?

The striving for such goals of prestige is often very obvious in children, particularly during the adolescent period. And naturally so. The child feels within him the awakening strength of his impulses, but he has not yet established his goals and especially his goals for the sex impulses in response to which his very flesh is changing. His beard is growing; his body shaping to the adult form. But the goal of the impulses that stir him lack full expression. He is surrounded by adults, superior in their experience, more assured in their goals. He cannot compete with them in accomplishment; he must obtain his satisfaction in prestige. And being a child with a child's naïveté, his egocentricity is crude and natural in expression: "See me do it. Watch me. I'm good!" Equally egocentric is his "showing off," particularly when strangers are present. When ignored—and that is the one thing no egocentric can endure—the child will often misbehave in order to obtain the ego titillation of prestige that comes from attention, even of a painful sort.

The actions of little Jean Blondell at the time her mother entertained the bridge club show to what extremes the youthful egocentric will go to obtain prestige. It was the custom of Mrs. Blondell, when the meetings were at her house, to exhibit Jean. For this egocentric purpose of her own the mother carefully groomed the child and primed her as to behavior. At the appropriate time the ladies made a most gratifying "fuss" over little Jean; she was patted and kissed and for some ten minutes occupied the center of attention.

Then, gently prodded by the smirking mother, she told the ladies "good-by" and went to the nursery. Usually she stayed there, but on this particular occasion she crept back into the room where the bridge games were in progress and hid in the big chair facing the hearth. She deliberately put her foot in the fire. Attracted by the smell of burning leather, one of the women sought for the source. She saw the child apparently being burned. Her scream brought all of the women to little Jean. Again the child occupied the center of attention, again she was petted and fondled and "fussed" over. She had again her moment of ego satisfying prestige.

The normal child in growing up gradually learns to establish true values for its endeavors. But some make little progress toward this end and remain egocentrics throughout life. Others fail to reach it fully and show in consequence some of the minor traits of egocentricity. Thus we find men with all degrees of egocentricity from those of the most blatant self-extollers, habitual braggarts, and drastic critics, down to those who show merely the most minor foibles, as does the man who never thinks of exploiting his success in business, a real success, but who praises himself on his triumphs in his minor avocations, golf or boating or bridge or fishing, and who in these directions is susceptible to flattery.

Such minor qualities of egocentricity are a nearly normal part of human behavior. There are few ladies indeed who do not take a pride in arousing the envy of their neighbors with the display of a new gown; there are few men who are above all vanities. Most people get a pleasure out of seeing their names in print, and newspaper editors are fully aware of the value of local names in increasing the popularity of their papers. Likewise hotel managers appeal to the same strain of egocentricity with the "personal touch" in their service. Furthermore, equally egocentric in its origin, there is, sad to say, for most of us a certain tinge of pleasure in the adversities of our best friends. Such very human traits are for most men only minor and incidental features of their lives. But for the true egocentric they are the very core of his existence.

Turning now to the more extreme manifestations of egocentricity, we find that there are three general avenues of approach along which the egocentric moves toward his goal of prestige. These we shall call the productive, self-constructive, and destructive approaches.

The egocentric who follows the productive way earns his prestige. He devotes himself to some accomplishment and strives for success. But his interest is not primarily in the success of the accomplishment; it is in the position, the fame that goes with it. He wants to be a famous man; he lives for fame.

The self-constructive egocentric chooses a less arduous road in obtaining his prestige. He is satisfied with a less well-grounded prestige. In fact, he manufactures it himself. He "builds himself up." His constructive efforts are directed toward impressing others with his importance.

The destructive egocentric arrives at the same end of false prestige, not by building himself up, but by "cutting down" the achievements of others. He minimizes the accomplishments of others to a level below his own so that he obtains, by contrast, a semblance of superiority. He is a "belittler." Often a destructive critic.

Frequently two and sometimes all three of the means of obtaining prestige are used by the individual egocentric, but more often his behavior is characterized by the predominance of one or another.

It is often difficult to differentiate the productive egocentric from the man who has merely a healthy ambition. Both in the end contribute to society, although the motives behind their efforts are different. The business field is not well suited to the display of the traits of the productive egocentric; because in this field personal fame and publicity are subordinated to profits. There

THE SOPHIST

From the English translation of the "Characters"
of Theophrastus

is, of course, no lack of egocentrics in business, but usually they are of the self-constructive or the destructive, rather than the productive, type.

Much more fertile fields for his cultivation of prestige lie in politics, writing, college teaching, the stage, the radio, science, military (the uniform), and especially religion (Protestant). Publicity is gained with comparative ease in all of these fields, and publicity brings satisfaction to the egocentric. In fact, anything that impresses his audience gives him this satisfaction. There are many preachers who, before assuming the cloth, have had great difficulty in deciding whether to be ministers or actors. Some of them would far rather meet their names in print than their parishioners in heaven. Their sermons are drafted with publicity in view.

With the author there is more reason than rationalization for publicity. Publicity sells books. But the egocentric author—and there are many such—may enhance his own ego in suitable circles with a remark beginning, "my recent book . . ." or even "the book I am thinking of writing." But his listeners must be those who do not know that except for a few inspired masters the writing of a book is merely a form of drudgery comparable to digging a ditch or doing the family wash, and often far less useful.

Besides the calling that he enters—and that, of course gives merely a hint of possible ego satisfaction—there are many little attributes that serve to differentiate the productive egocentric from the man of normal ambitions. The egocentric is prone to accept positions that are of little importance except for the titles attached to them; he may be keenly anxious to serve on committees and boards that afford no recompense except publicity. Furthermore, the productive egocentric—this is true of all egocentrics—shows an exaggerated resentment toward any criticism that threatens in the least to disturb his prestige. Not only is he intolerant of criticism, but he is unwilling to accept openly a suggestion from others even though it may contribute definitely toward his advancement. Sometimes he repudiates the idea; more often he deliberately devaluates it with some such remark as: "Yes, I had thought of that, but haven't got around to trying it yet." His resentment of advice gives to his behavior a peculiar sort of negativism often especially apparent in adolescent children. The egocentric may eventually utilize the suggestion, but he then refuses credit to its originator. In the productive egocentric this peculiarity, together with his unnatural desire for the prestige of accomplishment, leads him sometimes to plagiarize the ideas of others and with them to exploit himself. Such plagiarism occurs not only in the literary field, but particularly in that of science, into which many productive-egocentrics are drawn by the hope of fame that comes from new discoveries. To most scientists priority, credit, and prestige are indeed vital matters.

And credit, prestige, and publicity—they are goals of all productive egocentrics. It is to their advantage that the world by and large accepts men on the basis of their prestige.

The self-constructive egocentrics are more numerous by far than the productive. They are found in all walks of life and with all degrees of incidental productivity. They show all degrees of ingenuity in stalking their goal of prestige. They range from the clumsy open braggart of the street corner to the artistic *habitué* of the drawing-room; from the athlete who "plays to the grandstand" to the young lady who is always last to arrive at parties; from the girl with sporting proclivities, who advertises the fact by wearing her riding-habit when she goes shopping, to the grand dame who casually mentions her notable ancestors; from the affected, loud-voiced young lady who punctuates her commonplace conversation and shrill giggles by lisping a word or two of French or Italian, to the scholar who discusses erudite matters at the dinner table among guests ignorant of such subjects; from the soldier boy who struts in his uniform to the bride who demands that her husband pay constant court to her in public.

Open bragging is the simplest of the methods employed by the egocentric to inflate his ego; it is also the most obvious. Usually only the stupid are willing to expose their vanity openly, but some of the more intelligent egocentrics so far undervalue the perceptions of others—and that, of course, is in itself a characteristic trait—that they believe their audience fails to sense the bragging. But direct bragging, as all egocentrics soon learn, is a dangerous procedure; it always tends to arouse in those imposed upon a latent but nearly universal element of destructive egocentricity. We all have a desire to "cut down" the braggart and show him up in his true light. In consequence, the intelligent egocentric becomes wary and turns to safer and more subtle ways of bragging.

The simplest device is to drop the telltale "I" and share the cudos with a mythical partner as "we." A more indirect method is to bring self in only by inference by telling the exploits of great ancestors. Occasionally to further disguise the bragging, the ancestors are made to play humorous rôles; an acceptable excuse is thus afforded for telling the story: "It has been a family joke, you know. My great-grandmother stubbed her toe on Plymouth Rock when she landed from the *Mayflower*. It's just too funny! She would have fallen if Miles Standish hadn't caught her in his arms." Even an unpleasant rôle may be played by the ancestor, he may have been a pirate, but somewhere in the foreground is always the fact that he was either a very important or a very strong person. Again, many egocentrics develop an uncanny knack for making an opportunity to mention their college or their home town. "Naturally, I went to Harvard. Ours is an old Boston family, you know." Equally egocentric is the avowal of a lowly origin which makes the success of the individual even more striking. Many egocentrics have an amazing ability of leading the conversation around to themselves and then appear in the light of merely modestly answering questions about themselves. Still others do their bragging wholly by inference; they assume an authoritative air when discussing any question; they have special and inside information from important but confidential sources; they recount matters of common knowledge as if they alone were aware of the occurrences. Some are great spreaders of not overly reliable news; others are simply gossips. By far the subtlest form of bragging lies in the aggrandizement of friends and associates; the prestige is wholly by indirection. The egocentric's associates are remarkable men who accept him as an equal; therefore he too is a remarkable man.

It is to self-constructive egocentrics that all advertisements of self-development courses in conversation, music, and the like are directed. The advertisement that catches and holds the egocentric is the familiar one that plays upon the desire for social aggrandizement with testimonials to the effect: "I stepped into instant popularity. . . . I became the center of every crowd. . . . They laughed when I sat down, but weren't they surprised when I played the piano!" It is, also, among the egocentrics that the advertising genealogists find their easiest victims. What egocentric could resist the desire to have his ancestors traced back to William the Conqueror or Charlemagne? And have the genealogist's papers to prove it!

Following its devious ways the egocentric trait sometimes finds its outlet in the promising of favors, with no intention of bestowing. The apparent generosity attracts attention at the moment and subsequently, on the assumption that the promise has been kept, the egocentric receives credit for acts which he has not performed.

Thus Mrs. Joyce used this method in quite a harmless way in building up her prestige. Whenever she was present in a group her conversation bristled with such remarks as "My dear Margaret, George and I picked up the cutest little bracelet on our last trip to Naples. We got it just for you. If you could ever know what a terrible time we had getting it through the customs. I know you'll love it. I'll bring it over some night." "And, Elsie, I'm sewing, with my own hands, dear, a dress for that darling youngster of yours. I'll bring it over some afternoon. And you and John *must* come to dinner soon."

Mr. Joyce is not quite so harmless in his egocentricity. His promises made to his business associates and friends turn on doing them a favor by speaking in their interest to influential men and thus obtaining for them advancements and commissions. His favorite remark is: "Just leave it in my hands; I'll use my influence." And when, as must inevitably happen at times, the friends do obtain their desires—but through no efforts of his—he is the first on hand to remind them of his influence in their behalf.

Some egocentrics follow even a more subtle but none the less effective method than that of the Joyces. They exploit kindness and charity and derive a reputation for great goodness and tolerance. Mrs. Chester was of this type. She was a chronic defender. She couldn't believe that anyone she heard defamed was really bad or malicious. They were just misunderstood by everyone except herself. Everyone saw evil; she saw only good; that is where she differed from other people. Hers was often a superhuman perception, but from it she successfully exploited herself with the vicarious aid of people in whom she had in reality not the slightest interest.

Ostentatious charity is nearly always motivated by egocentricity—hence the publication of charity subscriptions—but it is only fair to add that egocentrics, even the destructive variety, may be kind and helpful to subordinates, in fact to all people whom they feel offer no threat to their prestige. The kindness is lost as soon as the subordinate becomes independent and hence a potential competitor. It is equally true that in the end the dollar given in ostentatious charity buys as much bread as the dollar given anonymously.

There are literally no limits to the extent to which some egocentrics will go to attract attention. Nor does the low quality of the attention deter them: They tell their life histories to hotel clerks; confide to shopgirls that they have just returned from Europe; to bootblacks that they are going to Washington; and to the Pullman porters that they are big men back in the towns where they come from. Some indeed appear to feel that any kind of attention, even the sort that most people find embarrassing, is preferable to no attention. Ignored at the tea party, they will drop their teacups on the floor for the sake of the momentary attention attracted by the crash of the crockery. They will inflict themselves with all sorts of uncomfortable eccentricities for the sake of the attention they hope to attract. They will break the ice to go swimming in the middle of winter if the newspaper photographers will attend. They will carry affectation to extremes in table manners, speech, and clothing. If their manners are criticized they often take refuge in a typically egocentric attitude of pretended indifference. "What do I care what people think of me?" But all who are eccentric in matters of dress and manners are not egocentrics; some are egoists. Their eccentricities are not motivated by a desire to attract attention, but by an absolute indifference to what anyone else may or may not think of them. They are equally indifferent to criticism, and unlike the egocentric do not bother to defend themselves.

When the egocentric limits the display of his peculiarities to a search for fame or even to actual self-inflation, he is rarely harmful, although he is often a nuisance or a bore. He becomes definitely harmful when his efforts are at the expense of some one else, when he "cuts down" others to obtain a pseudo eminence. The weapons of such a destructive egocentric are destructive criticism, ridicule, and the theft of prestige.

Destructive criticism may be a sort of negative bragging, and as in bragging the egocentric learns to follow devious paths in order that others may not see too clearly his true motives. Damning with faint praise gives the necessary camouflage for the more timid. They pull part of the sting from their criticisms by beginning with: "Yes . . . he's a good man, *but* . . ." or, "No doubt in her own way she is a very nice girl, *but* . . ." Often their voice unconsciously tricks them and exposes their real intent. The praise portion of their compound sentence is delivered slowly, almost in a questioning drawl, the "but" receives emphasis, and the destructive part of the sentence is readily noticed by the vigor of its delivery.

Still others of the more timid destructive egocentrics —and there is always an element of danger in destructive criticism—limit their remarks to those from whom there is little likelihood of retaliation, usually to men far above them in position. The office boy and the janitor can point out in no uncertain terms the inefficiencies of "the boss"; the second-rate boxer voices a low opinion of the champion; the young scientist expresses judicial doubt as to the real importance of some discovery of a famous contemporary; the interne points out (privately) the errors of the hospital's leading surgeon; and the man on the street tells with a wise air of his doubt concerning the policies and motives of some great statesman. The true egocentric is too wise to be fooled. And what satisfaction he has in contemplating the weaknesses and infirmities of the great! In fact, most of us are pleased to learn that Cleopatra was not beautiful, that Cæsar had fits, that Louis XIV had pyorrhea. For the egocentrics anyone who receives popular acclaim is a target; a fact that the authors of debunking books fully appreciate.

The more courageous destructive critics defame and belittle their own associates, but behind their backs. Usually they cover up their motives by a show of reticence: they dislike to say such things, but candor compels them—and it is amazing to what length of detail candor will at times force them against their avowed will. They rarely have difficulty in finding an audience.

Destructive criticism is a habit that grows on one almost imperceptibly. The well-developed destructive critic appears to obtain a sexlike gratification from his inveterate habit. It is a sort of mental masturbation in which energies are expended without producing anything. Perhaps in this vicarious satisfaction lies a partial explanation of the unproductiveness of many drastic literary and dramatic critics. Or perhaps it is the other way around; their drastic criticism takes its direction from their efforts to cover up their own impotency. In either event destructive criticism, whether it be in these fields or in the more common walks of life, the club, the office, the home, is invariably an identifying mark of the destructive egocentric.

The subordinate of an egocentric usually finds it impossible to obtain credit for his own accomplishments. If his accomplishments threaten the prestige of his superior they are suppressed or the credit stolen. The most obvious form of this behavior is seen on the stage. Actors, as might be anticipated, from their choice of career, are often egocentric and even some of the best are prone to "hog the stage" in order to detract from the lines of others. Many an eminent actor or actress has demanded the discharge of a subordinate whose talents were too highly appreciated by the audience. At the première of a recent production a famous actor of long-established reputation had in his cast a young lady who made an unexpected hit in the characterization of an impudent "flapper." Following the first burst of applause for her talent the leading actor began to play with and tease the dog she carried in her arms; by pantomime, while she was speaking, he did everything in his very considerable powers to attract attention from her to himself. Behavior with similar import is not limited to the stage; it is common in the drawing-room, the ballroom and the office.

All egocentrics, productive, self-constructive, destructive, are united both in their intolerance to criticism of themselves and in their susceptibility to flattery. The fairly well-balanced man appreciates sincere praise for his accomplishment; the novelty of it may startle him, but flattery, if he recognizes it as such, embarrasses or disgusts him. The egocentric accepts it as his due, for flattery is the food that feeds his own exaggerated opinion of himself. Indeed, he sometimes surrounds himself with flatterers—"yes men"—as was strikingly the case in the past with many egocentric kings. Along with the flattering courtiers there was not infrequently the apparently incongruous institution of the court jester who alone was permitted to criticize openly the king and his favorites. The jester, being a "fool" and frequently physically deformed as well, was in no possible way a competitor for prestige in his exhibitions in the royal circle. His "criticisms" covered with humor were regarded as absurd beyond reason; they were not considered serious or malicious. His was obviously a fool's opinion; wise men of necessity held the contrary. Even today the humorist in cartoon, in column, and on the stage, with his absurd extravagances that often cover biting sarcasms, is allowed much greater latitude in his remarks without offense than is the serious critic.

Susceptibility to flattery, as many have discovered, is the most vulnerable spot in the personality of the egocentric. He can rarely resist the desire to act out, and hence put the stamp of proof on flattering suggestions. In all walks of life he can be "worked" by flattery. The subordinate obtains favors by his open admiration of his egocentric superior; the young man adept at pleasing remarks is popular with many ladies; the mother gets her son to rake the leaves by telling him how strong he is; and even the child lifting its arms to the adult lisps "You're so big. Carry me!" And the adult does.

Chapter VII

THE MEEK, THE MILD, THE MILITANT (*Continued*)

I N COMPLETE contrast to the extreme egoists are those
meek souls of weak ego who we are told with dubious logic "will inherit the earth." Certainly they will acquire it in no other manner. In all human experience the
fruits of life are for those who struggle for them. The
egoists are abundant at the harvest.

The egocentric differs from the normal man in trying
too much to impress the world; the man of weak ego
differs from the normal man in being too much im-
pressed by the world. The man of weak ego senses his
own lack of strength; he overvalues the threat of his
environment and he feels impotent to cope with it. He
is unable to force his way into the environment and to
make a place for himself. He feels incapable of joining
freely in the normal give and take of life. Yet of all men
he has, and knows he has, the greatest need to feel himself a part of his environment; he is benefited most by
its protection. He wants above all else to be a part of the

[253]

group, to be accepted, for he feels eternally an outsider. He experiences the lonesomeness and the futility of life.

And yet these are sensations that are not wholly unknown to the normal man. He, too, may at times feel weak and sense keenly an overpowering threat in his environment. His strength may not always be the same. Ego strength may fluctuate within the individual just as does mood. The normally cheerful man can become angry and he can also become exhilarated; but when his anger or his exhilaration has passed he displays the average or fundamental mood that characterizes his individual temperament.

Similarly, each man has an average or fundamental ego strength. But his ego strength does not constantly remain at this one level. Instead it fluctuates within a range that rises above and falls below. Thus the normal man may have what are for him moments of especial ego strength and, correspondingly, moments of especial ego weakness. He may on occasions show minor traits of egocentricity, even egoism, and again minor traits of ego weakness. But the range of his vacillation is below the level of the true egoist and egocentric and above that of the weak in ego. His flights into egocentricity or egoism never reach the heights to which the true egoist may go; nor do his lapses into ego weakness descend to the depths into which those of true ego weakness fall.

Unquestionably these fluctuations in ego strength occur in response to variations in the activity of the deeply seated vital processes in which the impulse-life and moods are rooted. They are not limited to the normal man. In mood the irritable may have their moments of comfort and even the gloomy their ephemeral joys. So also the egocentric may have his moments of weakness when he doubts his strength and grows anxious. And the man of weak ego may experience at times an unexpected sense of peace and security, of acceptance, even of bravery. In such moments he may be emboldened to aggression, but his attacks are abortive. His strength passes and leaves him timid and afraid. There are some men in whom the fluctuations of ego strength are so regular and so profound as to be a characterizing feature of their personality. In respect to ego, they react as do those individuals whose fundamental temperament shows wide fluctuations, mood-swings. But instead of being alternately exhilarated and depressed they exhibit in turn aggression, even marked egocentricity, and, then without apparent cause, the fears and timidities of ego weakness.

Timidity, self-consciousness, and sensitivity have

their origin in ego weakness; from it arise also some of the most unreasonable forms of human behavior. But timidity and self-consciousness are qualities that all normal men experience and show in some degree. There are modifying factors that serve to differentiate their timidity from that of the man of weak ego.

Timidity, whether only experienced or also shown, is invariably an indication that the immediate environment is felt as a threat. But no absolute value can be set upon the threat; it is always a personal and relative matter. Each man gauges the strength of his environment against his own strength; he puts his individual valuation on each situation. But a common environment may not offer an equal threat to all men even if they possess the same strength of ego.

The normal child who shows a healthy egocentricity in the well-experienced environments of home and school may, when taken to his first party, or when confronted by a group of strangers, show an equally healthy timidity and self-consciousness. But after many parties and many meetings with strangers his timidity is lost. He has responded to social training. But in acquiring this training and losing his timidity the fundamental strength of his ego has not been altered. These particular situations through experience have for him merely lost their threat.

But all children do not show an equal timidity in encountering new experiences, nor do all lose their timidity with equal readiness. Each child's ego strength plays a part in shaping his individual reactions. Consequently some are bold from the very beginning and some retain their shyness and self-consciousness in spite of many experiences. Between these extremes there are also all gradations.

The values placed upon a situation by the individual have, like experience, a modifying influence upon the threat of the environment. The clerk entertaining at dinner his supervisor—his superior—places on the situation a set of values entirely different from those that the general manager would place on it if it were he who were entertaining the supervisor—his inferior. And yet on the different levels given by their respective positions each clerk and each manager—and for that matter each supervisor as well—views the situation and reacts to it strictly in accord with his individual ego endowment.

Since there can be no absolute measure of ego strength, it must always be evolved with some general average of human reactions in view. And the normal or average man must serve as this point of reference.

The common environment of our civilization has been developed, as we have said, to suit the ego strength of the average, and therefore presumably normal, man. Certainly this environment does not meet the desires of the egoist, nor is it the most comfortable one for display of the egocentric's peculiarities. Neither is it suited to the needs of the man of weak ego. He senses its threat more keenly than the normal man, and his reactions to it differ. It is this difference that marks him as being of weak ego. The man of weak ego reacts to the community of normal men as a normal man would react if he were placed in a community of egoists.

The normal man so placed would feel the superior strength and aggression of those about him. He would be unable to compete with others on an equal basis. There would be only two courses of behavior open to him: he could either give up the struggle to force his way and surrender, or else, resenting the situation and refusing to surrender, he would go away, flee from the competition. And in essence those are precisely the ways in which the man of weak ego reacts in a community of men of normal ego strength.

Of course his behavior lacks the elementary simplicity

and directness that is explicit in the choice of reactions given here. His surrender is indirect; his isolation incomplete. But in either case there is a sufficient similarity to allow the classification of those of weak ego into two groups—the submissive and the resentful.

And by a saving grace of normal men there is also a third way that the weak of ego may follow, one into which the average man placed in a community of egoists would find no satisfaction, for its success depends upon qualities that are not found among egoists—warmth and sympathy. The man of weak ego can, in the normal community, take on the rôle of a wounded person, wounded by the unjust barbs of those about him, and as wounded he may have especial allowances made for him. Many men weak of ego are sensitive in high degree to all slights and rebuffs, but there are some in whom this sensitivity dominates their whole behavior. They are mistrustful; they feel persecuted. And their perceptions are so exquisitely acute that they can see affront and offense where none exist. They never forgive or forget. Their fragile structure requires the gentlest handling—and often they receive it. Such we shall class as the sensitive.

The Submissive.—The submissive are the eternal underlings who look to their superiors for support and shelter. They are the "yes men" whose apparent faith and devotion arise not from love, but from weakness. They are men who exhibit no ambition for advancement because ambition would throw them into conflict with men of stronger ego, and advancement would lift them to an exposed and unprotected position, one from which they could not escape responsibility and the dangers that responsibility involves. Sometimes they are weakly resentful in their submission; and sometimes they glory in it and make a virtue of it. It is they who turn the other cheek to be slapped; but they turn it often with ostentation.

Religion as an institution of shelter may be ideally suited to those who have the submissive characteristics of ego weakness. Religion often provides an environment in which they find an ego satisfaction. The meek are not wholly devoid of pride, neither are they always anxious to display their weakness; rather, like the egocentric, they prefer to disguise it. In religion they may find self-respect. Their self-abnegation is viewed as an admirable quality. It is mistaken for strength held in curb. There is pride in meekness, for do not the meek inherit the earth? Is not eternal salvation for the humble? The Christian religion of the New Testament, perhaps more than most, preaches humbleness; the Old

Testament—barring a few such incidents as Job's amazing ego weakness—is remarkably free from the precept of self-abnegation—"an eye for an eye and a tooth for a tooth."

And yet among the submissive there is often an element of egocentricity, pride in the prestige of meekness. The martyr's prestige: "See, I sacrifice myself. I sacrifice myself for others. I give more than others. Behold me!"

There is no doubt a certain pleasure in being a martyr. Nor do all martyrs act only upon the great stages of life; there are everyday martyrs, household martyrs. They, too, make their feeble appeals for prestige of a sort. Some whine and snivel and complain; some affect an air of sublime resignation with just a drooping mouth to show their sorrow and a bended back to show the load they carry. But either variety resents assistance in the task by which they make themselves martyrs.

Mrs. Bissell was of the sublime variety of martyrs and many were the responsibilities from which her self-imposed martyrdom saved her. Mr. Bissell was a clerk in a large concern dealing in paper and twine. Each year the employees held a picnic; Mr. Bissell always went, but he went without Mrs. Bissell. He dutifully asked her to go, but from long years of experience he knew her reply before she gave it and he knew the falling inflection at the end of each short sentence in her tired soft voice: "You go if you wish, George. Yes, I want you to go. I want you to enjoy yourself. But you know *I* can't go. My duty is at home."

George Bissell caused her far less trouble than most husbands do their wives, but the neighbors regarded him as unreasonably severe, and for good cause. He was always Mrs. Bissell's excuse for getting out of responsibilities: "George," so she said, "didn't want her to work for the church supper. . . ." "George wouldn't like her to have the Ladies' Aid Society meet at her house. . . ." George wouldn't. . . . And always with her sad, resigned air. In reality George knew nothing of these matters.

There is only one child, but that fact does not keep Mrs. Bissell from speaking of him as "the children," nor had Mr. Bissell's protests kept her from naming the child Elmer. "You can name him what you will," she had said. "That is a father's privilege, but to me he will always be Elmer." Mrs. Bissell had her way; she always did, sweetly and resignedly.

Elmer was a great comfort to his mother and a great trial, a terrible responsibility—"all children were great responsibilities to the mother who sacrificed her life for them, as a mother should." But then in Elmer she lived over the happier moments of earlier days. Elmer was still her baby, even though he was sixteen now. She thrilled to his lavish caresses even as she had when as a baby she put him to her breast. Elmer was to her what George might have been if George had not become unappreciative and indifferent to the sacrifices she made. The boy was weakly resentful and surly to his father. The mother and the son spent many hours talking over the defects of the father; the boy frankly antagonistic, the mother urging him on with half-denials and sighs and shrugs.

Elmer had for his mother one of those abnormal attachments to which the weak of ego are prone. Weak ego is the soil in which such complexes flourish; never—it is incredible on the face of it—could a true egoist have an Œdipus complex. Such peculiarities in character formation cannot be produced with equal ease in all personalities. The inherent elements of personality play a part as well as environment in shaping character. Elmer had inherited his mother's weak ego. Mother was his realm of security.

For Mrs. Bissell submission solved most problems.

But submission did not solve those of Mr. Trusk. You see, he had to live with Mrs. Trusk. There was nothing weak about her ego; she was a household tyrant who made her henpecked husband's life almost, but not quite, unbearable, for Henry Trusk continued to bear it. She had made him miserable for nineteen years. That the neighbors knew, and they knew also that Henry Trusk's "boss" dominated him at the office nearly as much as his wife did at home. But what they did not know was Henry's resentment and that each day he made two resolutions. All the way to the office he rehearsed in private the devastating speech that he was going to deliver to his boss as soon as he reached the office, and all the way home at night he rehearsed the devastating speech that he was going to deliver to his wife. Neither has ever been delivered, for in a way that Mr. Trusk cannot understand the courage oozes out of him with the cold perspiration of anxiety each time he hears his "boss" call, "Here, Trusk!" or his wife's "Henry!"

During many a night of insomnia Henry Trusk has rehearsed the whole situation. He knows to the very core of him, that if he were to "face his boss" and talk as man to man, demanding his rights, he would get them. His "boss" is a reasonable man, but he gives no more than is asked. Henry has never been able to ask. The mere imagination of the scene fills him with a panic of anxiety. He hasn't had a raise in eleven years; other

men who do the same work he does get twice as much
as he. His wife, and he knows that, too, would cease
to nag him, she would even admire him, if he would
face her boldly and determinedly. He has seen her yield
to other people. But he can't demand; he is a timid soul.
He can't even run away, though he has often thought
of it. If he ran away, there is no telling what difficulties
he might get into; things might be worse than they are
now. He has even wished his wife would die and his
"boss" would die, but that, too, might bring difficulties.

All his life people have "picked" on Henry Trusk.
Since he was a small boy he has been the "butt" of
every cruel joke of his associates. People like him, he is
modest, and quiet and friendly. But also they sense his
weakness, sense the fact that he will not retaliate when
they deride him. It is safe; he offers no threat. One does
not in safety play practical jokes on the egoist.

Mrs. Beale is weak of ego but she is neither a martyr
nor yet resentful of her submission. She's a cheerful
little woman who simply can't make up her own mind
and can't refuse anyone anything. She is the target for
every beggar and every salesman. Both bully her on
sight. She can be forced to purchase anything. She finds
it impossible to resist the clerks in the stores. First she
asks their advice. They tell her what she should buy.

It is not what she had intended to purchase, but she buys it, anyway. Her only protection is a charge account; she can send the purchases back after they are delivered.

And Emma, that is Mrs. Beale's maid, has not only a weak intellect, but a weak ego as well, a submissive ego, submissive to religion of a kind. No one knows anything of Emma's past, for there is only one subject on which Emma will talk—religion. In the three years she has been with Mrs. Beale she has belonged to four different creeds, none of which Mrs. Beale had ever heard of before and all of which were temporary cults in the hands of fanatical leaders.

At present her whole conversation has a distinctly communistic trend, for Emma in her ignorance has mistaken the fevered propaganda of a radical group for a religious revival. She is blissful in her ignorance, for the tenets of the propaganda are quite as comforting as those of the religions to which she has been accustomed. In the one previous to her present commitment she had heard in the dingy and dusty quarters of a side-street vacant store lighted with unshaded lamps, of a hand that stretched from heaven to protect her in all her earthly plights. This same hand by some strange metamorphosis also was to give her the strength to be humble to the "children of the world." The combination of protection with condescension on her part was particularly pleasing to Emma's ego.

For a time all of her discussions of menus with Mrs. Beale were liberally blessed with verbal gestures from "the hand." But the store was rented and the "preacher" moved along to a distant town. Three blocks away another meeting was in progress; she found a welcome and a chair. Here she heard that religion and honor and patriotism were things of the past, weapons by which the worthy were downtrodden to the will of the unworthy. Emma could not quite understand the connection, but the part about the downtrodden struck a responsive note. There was to be a sharing of wealth; every man was to be rich; none was to exceed another; all were to work together and each was to receive the same wage. There was to be equality! It was all very gratifying to a weak ego.

Emma told Mrs. Beale of some of the new precepts that had come into her life, and Mrs. Beale was a little frightened, for she thinks Emma is a fanatic and "fanatics may be dangerous, you know." But Emma is no fanatic and she never will be; she is simply an ardent follower of fanatics who tout to the desires that stir in egos that are weak. Three nights out of seven she attends the meetings in a remote part of town. She walks both to and from the place, for Emma never rides on street cars or trains, nor does she answer the telephone. The other nights she spends silently in her room. The entire Beale household is run on a rigid time-table that corresponds with Emma's extensive and varied "religious" observations. But Mrs. Beale puts up with her; Mrs. Beale would put up with anyone.

The Resentful.—The submissive find through their very submission a place in the environment. They are underlings but as such they are at least allowed to follow along with the group. They are useful. They are accepted.

The resentful cannot so completely surrender themselves. Their ego strength is too great for that, but it is too little to allow them to make a place for themselves. They want to be taken in, to be accepted, to be given an important place even though they have made no valid effort to gain this privilege. They are always conscious of themselves in relation to others; they are often highly critical of the attitudes of others toward them.

Of all men the egoist is certainly least conscious of himself in relation to others; he ignores them. The egocentric is continually conscious of the relation; in fact, his whole attention is focused upon it. But he is not

self-conscious in the commonly accepted meaning of
the term. Quite the contrary. He continually courts
attention. He seems to say: "See me! See what I am
doing. See how well I am getting along." In short, he
"feeds" his ego with the attention of his audience.

It is the man of weak ego, particularly the resentful
type, who exhibits the timidity and embarrassment of
self-consciousness. His attitude toward the regard of
others is one of anxiety and uncertainty. If he were to
express in words his relation to the group he would say
in effect: "How am I getting along? I feel I'm doing
badly. I wish I could feel comfortable and at ease and
be free and natural with other people. I want people to
notice me and like me. But people don't pay much
attention to me." But never, in public at least, could he
thus express himself freely and frankly. He would be
embarrassed; his remarks would be strained and even
tactless. After each forced sally into the conversation
he quickly takes refuge in quietness and resentment.
Nor would his self-consciousness cease when the day
was done; he would take to bed with him his whole
relationship with his environment to think it over but
never to reach a solution. The tendencies in life of the
man with this type of ego weakness are those of abortive attacks, resentments, and retreats. Comfortable easy

adjustment is impossible for him. He can never "forget himself." Instead in all of his relations he remains continually critical and continually self-conscious. Instead of joining wholeheartedly in the activities of the group, giving himself, submerging himself, he stands to one side. Such thoughts as these come to his mind: "I am not receiving attention. No one seeks me out. I'm being neglected. I feel insignificant and futile. These people wouldn't miss me if I were not here. If only they would give me the popularity and admiration I deserve I would put all my personal interests in the background and give all of myself and all of my time to the group. But they snub me when I try to give. I want to be nice, but I am rebuffed. When people are nice to me I am too friendly and that seems to frighten them away. When they don't give me the attention I deserve I become quiet and they don't bother with me. Perhaps these things happen because I don't like people. People bother me; they put a strain on me. They won't accept what I give. I have every reason for resentment. I don't want to be in with this crowd. What I really want is to be on the outside as an observer, a critical observer. I want to retire and work out my problems alone. I shall withdraw; I shall isolate myself." Such is the monotonous, insistent circuity of his reasoning on his relations to his environment.

And so it goes through life—weak attack, imagined rebuff, resentment, retreat; and then again attack, rebuff, retreat. . . . Men of this ego weakness are like turtles in their behavior, but without the turtle's snap. A head is cautiously pushed out from under the shell; it receives a tap from the environment or perhaps there is only a gesture in its direction; but back under the shell goes the head; then again it protrudes and is withdrawn. Instead of staying out and taking the taps and rebuffs it retreats—continually retreats. Alone in the shell it pities itself, and there in isolation it finds fault with the world; but it finds no satisfaction with itself and so out again it goes, but doomed to defeat.

Charles Hibbens carried with him this turtle-like behavior to preparatory school. He roomed alone. He wanted a roommate, but none of the boys asked him to room with them. Neither did he ask anyone to room with him. But the only fact that remained in his mind was that no one had asked him. He felt left out.

Charles came of a prominent family in a small town. He believed that on this account, if no other, his schoolmates would be glad that he was with them. But at dinner, where the new boys sat thirty to a table, none seemed conscious of his presence as he stiffly waited for some one to address him. Instead they were engrossed with their own interests; finding out each other's names, their schools, their towns; discovering mutual friends and joking over the food. He felt left out.

No one had asked him about his family! Finally a youngster across the table called to him: "Hey! Where are you from?" Charles would have liked to fling back an easy gibe that would have set the table in an uproar. Instead, as anxiety gripped him, he said: "I'm from Barrie. My father owns the factory there." The boy across the table—a budding egocentric—shouted with hysterical joy: "Hey, fellows, here's a guy whose father has a berry factory! Pie for us? Eh!"

Charles was rebuffed; a wave of self-pity swept over him. He was quiet until the end of the meal, and then he retired to his room. Into the small hours of the morning he thought over the situation and came to this conclusion: he could never be as one with these boys. He took life seriously; they did not. But he would show them. They would be glad to accept him and give him the respect he deserved. He would be an author! He had heard that authors were sensitive and critical spectators of life. And these boys would read his books and magazine articles; they would seek him out and treat

im with respect and admiration. They would give a
dinner for him and he would sit at the head of the
able and everyone there would rise in turn and say
complimentary things about him. They would give him
. medal. But in the meantime it was frightfully lone-
ome up in his room. At home the family—at home!
The talons of nostalgia dug at the weak vitals of
Charles, and he sobbed himself to sleep.

Of course Charles never wrote the books; in the first
place he wrote badly even for a schoolboy, so badly
hat he did not submit stories to the school magazine.
But that fact did not prevent him from planning the
book each time that he felt the group had rebuffed him,
and that was often. The great book was to be about a
young man who had a tragedy in his life—a young man
who was misunderstood by other people; who did not
get the attention he deserved in life and who, because
of this lack of appreciation, took a trip in a boat. Although the young man did not know it at the time
the boat was to be shipwrecked on a deserted island and
the only two passengers to reach shore were to be the
misunderstood hero and a young lady—very beautiful—
who had secretly admired him on the boat. The life
on the island was also to be very, very beautiful—a
sort of Eden free from snakes and particularly free from

groups, from other men who could possibly compete with the hero for the favors of the extremely complaisant and extremely admiring young lady. Of course if she had shown interest in other men she would have been unworthy of Charles' hero and the hero would have left her and lived alone on another island.

Charles read a great many books of this kind; in fact he read so many during the first term that his school grades suffered badly in consequence.

Men have done great deeds from the stimulus of a conviction of inferiority. They have compensated, or more than compensated, for their deficiency. They have actually written the "book" to show their companions that they could. But many, even with the stimulus, never make the full effort.

Some merely try to cover up, to conceal their sense of insecurity by a brave front, a bluff on the principle that the best defense is an attack. These are mechanisms, complexes, built into character and hence beyond the scope of our discussion except to this extent: ego weakness is the fertile soil in which these complexes flourish.

But Charles Hibbens does not and cannot disguise his ego weakness and his resentments. What he does not know and what he never could be made to understand is that he does not give of himself. He expects rewards to be handed to him without the effort of striving for them. In consequence he will always be an outsider; he will be left out of the clubs and fraternities; left out of the dances and parties. The fact is that if he were taken in he would contribute nothing to their success. He would be too concerned with his precious ego, too concerned in protecting himself against rebuffs, too concerned with what others might think of him, and too concerned with his fears and resentments.

Many people of weak ego submit to great inconveniences in preference to demanding their rights. They go to far greater efforts in evading issues than would be required in facing them squarely. Their difficulty goes back to their fundamental inability to adjust properly to others. And this lack of adjustment applies not only to the group of their associates, but to those in all the walks of life. They cannot, and they know they cannot, lose their self-consciousness when they speak to the ticket agent, the hotel clerk, the Pullman porter, the chauffeur, the waiter, the servant. They cannot express their requirements with friendly dignity. If they are friendly, the servant might have a low opinion of them; if they demand, he might refuse to obey. Consequently they are resentful when he does not anticipate their wants. They are never sure of their judgments and their decisions. They wish to tell the chauffeur to drive slower, but it might be possible that the chauffeur would give some valid reason for driving at his present speed. An issue would arise. They would be forced to make definite demands or else admit defeat. Either would be painful. Moreover, they are very conscious of what the chauffeur might think of them. They are concerned with everyone's opinion. Consequently it would be better not to raise the issue, but instead accept the disagreeable situation. And then if by chance they found an opportunity to condemn the chauffeur for his wholly unintentional fault they would do so. Many a man of weak ego has damned a taxicab line, a hotel, a railroad and even a servant for faults that would willingly have been remedied if a word had been spoken.

But the word, the correct combination of ease and assurance, of a quietly dignified, but firm request, is beyond the powers of him of the weak ego. The submissive man may ingratiate himself and plead, but that the resentful man cannot do. He is stiff, inflexible, ill-at-ease. If he takes a stand he is as often as not unjust in his demands, has chosen the wrong time to make an issue of the matter. He blusters, pumps himself up to a rage he does not truly feel, delivers his speech and retires hastily, resentfully. Often he must immediately tell some one of his resentment and seek their backing and their support in his opinion. If they fail to agree with him, he retires still more deeply into his shell of resentment and aloofness.

George Dreufus rides frequently from a suburban town into a city some eighty miles away. Each time he watches intently the Pullman porter as he collects the baggage and brushes the coats and hats, to see that his own are cared for at the proper time. Always he has a feeling that others are receiving better attention than he. He is fearful that on some trip the porter will forget his hat and coat and that he will have to take them down from the rack himself or that he will have to carry out his own bag in front of other people and thus exhibit his neglect. He resents the impartial way the porter treats him; resents, too, the way the porter waits on those who ring for him or ask his assistance. He never asks the porter for anything. He resents him, but he always tips him. The porter might have a low opinion of him if he fails to tip. The unspoken and unjust protest finds its outlet in the size of the tip. It is very small.

In other situations his tips are large; an aggressive waiter can, with a scornful look, make him add coins to those he has left on the plate. But after such an

[277]

experience he can never again eat in the restaurant where it has occurred. And he never forgets such matters.

To George Dreufus beggars on the street are an especial trial; they put him in a quandary. If he brushes them aside they may have a low opinion of him; if he gives them money they may think he is gullible. Either attitude is distasteful to him. He will cross to the opposite side of the street if he sees a beggar and he is continually on the watch for them.

Every situation in life affects him as do the beggars. He wants others to have a high opinion of him, and yet he fears to be exploited. In his uncertainty he continually protects himself; his protection is only a false aloofness and an evasion of all issues.

Often those of weak ego succeed in finding an environment in which from long association they feel a measure of freedom and ease. Some actually construct such an environment, one intended to avoid competition. They surround themselves with associates whom they feel are inferior to them, financially or socially inferior. The admiration and envy they receive for their superiority they accept as intended for themselves. It gives them a gratifying sense of security.

Such was the case with Mary Dodge. From childhood she had been a difficult child. In fact, all of the children in the Dodge family—there were three—had been difficult. But at first it was impossible to tell how much of the disturbance arose from the environment and how much was inherent in the basic components of their personalities. The Dodges were wealthy, very wealthy, and very exclusive. They were a serious, quiet, soft-spoken people, rarely seen in public and rarely entertaining in the dark house that stood surrounded by a park at the edge of town.

Mary, her sister, and her brother, were trained by servants and tutors, as subdued, soft-voiced, and quiet as the children themselves. The training was not good and the children were not particularly bright. The girls went to exclusive finishing-schools; the boy with great difficulty got into college. He was an "outsider" from the very beginning. His draft into the expeditionary forces of the World War came to him as a momentary relief, but he developed shell shock in the debarkation camp and committed suicide in the military hospital. The sister died of tuberculosis. The mother and father died soon afterwards. And Mary was left alone with her inheritance: a great fortune and a weak ego.

At the age of twenty-nine she married a playwright. Her ego weakness nearly wrecked the marriage within a year. She felt that her husband had married her for her money, although this was definitely not the case. She felt also that he looked in contempt upon her lesser intellectual abilities. Unable to face the issue and thrash it out with him, she took refuge in petty resentments. She refused to spend any of her money, refused to meet his friends; she pretended jealousy; sexually she was frigid; she isolated herself from all social obligations.

The husband, a tactful, complacent man, sincerely fond of his wife and distressed at her peculiarities, finally prevailed upon her to see a psychiatrist. He made an appointment for her with a prominent physician. She refused to keep the appointment, left town, and put herself into the hands of a woman practitioner of psychoanalysis—a well-qualified and highly competent individual.

The analyst was vastly familiar with Mary's type. Most of her patients had the same fundamental ego disturbance. In fact, the principles underlying her therapeutic measures had been evolved largely from the behavior of those with weak egos. She knew exactly what would be revealed in the conferences: the feeling of futility; the difficulty of adjustment; the sense of being unable to become a part of the group; the resentment; the desire for isolation; the desire for popularity; the feeling of unpopularity and so on and on in the usual vein of ego weakness.

A fixation on the brother was uncovered, and with it a feeling of guilt that in some way she might be responsible for his suicide.

Deftly the analyst steered the disclosures. In return she gave a crutch for Mary's weak ego.

The crutch was this: Mary in the analysis faced her issues. The facts of her life—at least the facts as she saw them—were brought out into the open. Clearer and clearer it seemed to her that there were many deep-seated complexes in her unconscious mind, over which she had no control, that gave her the fears and resentments she experienced. An explanation was given for her anxieties. She now had a reason for her reaction to the environment. And with the reasons came a certain sense of security.

With the crutch given her Mary set about remaking her life. She and her husband moved from the city to a small town where there were few wealthy people and very little civic activity. For a year Mary made her way cautiously. Slowly she became acquainted with the townsmen and their wives. She chose a circle from among those who obviously admired her and envied her and were willing to work with and for her. With the group she felt secure. On gaining this security she launched a campaign of social-service work. She directed its inception largely from the background, but no one in the town had the slightest doubt of her part in it. Most of the townswomen, although they exhibited no great enthusiasm for the social-service work, showed a gratifying willingness to be associated with her. There was a prestige attached to the association. She was wealthy, she was cultured, she came of a prominent family.

The campaign well under way, Mary took a fervid interest in personally distributing supplies to the needy. This rôle of Lady Bountiful gave her a comfortable and flattering feeling of being an important part of the group—admired, secure, giving a real and accepted value to the environment.

Mary has created this environment which, like cotton batting, surrounds her delicate ego and shields it from the rebuffs of a rude world. Outside of it, perhaps even within it, anyone unblinded by the setting would still recognize the weak ego—for it is unchanged in spite of all her efforts. The continual self-consciousness is still there, the impossibility of facing issues, the evasion of all possible public statements before a group, the extreme agitation when they are inescapable, the petty resentments and unnecessary rudeness for tiny or imagined rebuffs.

When the weak of ego gain a feeling of security they sometimes develop with it a peculiar type of aggressiveness. It usually takes the form of rudeness. In surroundings in which they feel insecure they experience resentment, but they dare not show it. But when they feel that they have the support and backing of others—as in the case of Mary Dodge—they may risk the display. Consequently, they may be cuttingly rude especially to those who they believe are not in favor with the group. But, as would be expected, there is no depth or stamina to their aggression. It crumbles in the face of a counter-attack. Those of weak ego can be "annihilated" by anyone who calls them sternly to account for their rudeness.

The Sensitive.—Anyone with ego weakness may exhibit sensitivity in some degree. But there are certain individuals in whom this quality is the dominating peculiarity in the expression of their ego weakness. Such are classed as the sensitive.

The essential and characteristic feature of sensitivity lies in a peculiar linking of ego weakness with mood and emotion. The sensitive, when their environment seems to threaten them, respond with an emotional reaction. They develop an inner tension. Their mood changes. They experience an uncomfortable and disagreeable sensation, usually one of depression. In consequence of its emotional origin, their reaction to any threat is immediate. It is also extreme. And it is involuntary.

Lacking this emotionality that the sensitive show, the weak of ego must think out rather than feel out their relation to the environment. They must balance one observation against another, study each situation to determine the nature and extent of the threat it offers. The sensitive, on the contrary, do not need to think about it. They feel the threat. They respond with their peculiar reaction to many situations in which any deliberation would show them that no threat was intended. But of this fact they cannot be convinced. Their sensations tell them that the threat does exist.

In the periods between their temperamental reactions the sensitive show no characteristic fundamental mood. They may normally be cheerful, but they are more often anxious or gloomy. The gloomy mood usually carries with it some degree of sensitivity. The gloomy are easily wounded, but they do not all possess the exquisite vulnerability of the true sensitive. The sensitive are rarely fundamentally irritable and never explosive, for these two temperamental peculiarities are associated with stronger impulses than the sensitive possess.

Whatever the prevailing mood of the sensitive may be, it is altered at the moment when they sense the threat of their environment. They have mood-swings. But their mood-swings are fundamentally different from those of men whose temperaments are defined as moody. Usually in such individuals mood alters in response to changes originating primarily in the vital processes of their own bodies. The mood of the sensitive, on the contrary, alters in response to changes originating primarily in the environment.

The immediate reaction of the sensitive to the sensations they experience is varied. Never, however, do they give vent to violent outbursts of resentment. At most they protest and bicker. Sometimes they are feebly querulous and sometimes they become haughty. But far more often they are merely depressed and silent—wounded.

Regardless of the nature of their immediate response, the sensitive always cherish a lasting self-pity. With tenacity they cling to the memory of their affront. It and everything about it remains always associated in their minds with the unpleasant sensation they have experienced. They rarely fail soon to find an opportunity to express their disapproval of those who have wounded them. They neither forget nor do they wholly forgive. Years after the occurrence, when its memory has passed from the minds of everyone else, the sensitive will recall it and brood over it.

To their friends and families the sensitive are often a sore trial. They have an uncanny talent of making others seem always in the wrong, a weapon they use unsparingly in obtaining their own ways and in making themselves the "weak tyrants" of the households. In dealing with the sensitive it is embarrassing to feel that one has been so clumsy as to commit a breach of etiquette, to give an unintentional wound. And it is annoying to be continually on guard for fear that the sensitive will find cause for offense in any chance remark or action.

Great tact is needed in dealing amicably with the sensitive. Almost literally they must be approached with apologies. But approached they must be, for the slightest neglect is to them as much a cause of offense as is an active affront.

But it is, after all, the sensitive themselves who suffer more than their associates. It is they who feel the wound. It is also they who wish the more to avoid it. In consequence as a sort of protection many of the sensitive exploit their peculiarity. They let it be known that they are delicate, touchy, easily offended, and hence deserving of especially careful handling. This saving information is in turn passed along by their friends to each new group that the sensitive encounters. In this regard such expressions as these are commonplaces: "Be careful of Agnes; she is such a sensitive child." Or, "Look out for John; he's terribly touchy."

But in spite of all efforts to follow such warnings, the sensitive are invariably wounded. They are mistrustful, often suspicious. Frequently those who give the offense are sincerely ignorant of the triviality which has called forth the emotional reaction. It may have been a word, a look, a movement, even a pause in the conversation that has disturbed the delicately balanced emotions which pivot about the ego of the sensitive.

Thus it took only a gesture, and a gesture made in the best of intentions, to break up the friendship between Margaret Holman and Mrs. Cabbott.

Margaret was sensitive. She was also highly talented musically. Her playing, while perhaps lacking in aggression, was rich and deep in feeling. But she was a temperamental musician. She was hurt by the slightest lack of consideration, by the merest suggestion of criticism.

And when hurt she became depressed; she withdrew and went quietly to her home. Her extreme reactions to her audiences and critics had ruined for her an otherwise promising concert career. And this same sensitivity was carried into every phase of her social life.

Following a dinner at the house of Mrs. Cabbott, who up to then was one of Margaret's most intimate friends, she was asked to play. All but one of the dozen guests present knew of Margaret's sensitivity. They sat rigidly silent during her brief performance. But one, a brother of the hostess, visiting from out of town, started to rise, intending to move to a more comfortable chair. His sister, near the piano, motioned him to be quiet. Margaret, from the corner of her eye, saw the motion. Mistrustful of the intent of the gesture behind her back, her sensitivity was touched upon; she experienced an inner tension and a sudden change of mood. She finished the piece she was playing and, although urged to continue by her hostess, she declined on the grounds of fatigue. Her gloomy expression gave support to the statement that she was tired.

Mrs. Cabbott, called to the other end of the room, lost sight of Margaret for a moment. But knowing the symptoms of her peculiarities, certain that she was hurt, but totally unaware of the cause, Mrs. Cabbott hastened back. But Margaret was gone. She had hurriedly obtained her wraps and left the house. Mrs. Cabbott threw up her hands in some mock and yet in some real despair. She knew the probable trend of Margaret's subsequent comments: The Cabbotts were inconsiderate; they entertained impossible people; she would never again play at their house. Whatever Margaret's remarks may have been, the fact remains that she and Mrs. Cabbott have ceased to be intimate friends. When they meet now there is always an aloofness in Margaret's manner.

As would be expected, the sensitive cannot in safety be teased. So long as the play of wits can be kept wholly impersonal, they may respond with an amusing display of repartee. But if the slightest personal note, the slightest criticism, creeps into the exchange—and it always does, for the sensitive can always infer some reference to themselves—the humor ceases. The sensitive then become serious. They may even retaliate for the imagined affront with a bickering sort of resentment.

Such was the case with the Reverend Doctor Chester. He was the head of a large educational and philanthropic foundation. He was also a witty and brilliant speaker, much in demand for banquets at schools and colleges. He accepted the invitations freely, but made one condition: he should be last on the program. Few people knew that this demand of the apparently jovial executive was based upon the fact that he was exquisitely sensitive to any criticism of his policies. If he were last on the program there was no one to comment on his statements; and being last, he could retaliate if any of the previous speakers had chanced to touch him in a tender spot.

On the occasion of a college banquet given by an undergraduate association, one of the students on the program was a serious-minded, well-intended, but not overly tactful young gentleman. In the course of an earnest but stumbling speech he made several references to the way the younger generation would handle educational policies when, as would soon be the case, they took over the reins. His talk was amateurish, it was naïve, it was adolescent, and it was also somewhat egocentric. By anyone of well-balanced ego it would have been taken as expressing merely these juvenile phenomena rather than any criticism worthy of serious consideration. But not so the Reverend Doctor Chester. Instead of giving the witty and withal keenly philosophical talk which he was expected to deliver and which he had actually prepared, he devoted a half-hour to tearing the younger speaker verbally limb from limb. It was an embarrassing spectacle. And the more so because the voice of the Reverend Doctor Chester carried a tinge of bitter emotion that engendered an uneasiness among his auditors.

In all his relations with his subordinates Doctor Chester shows this same immediate and exaggerated resentment to criticism. He often detects criticism where none is intended. At times he appears to feel almost persecuted.

Harold Johnson, who is an architect, has this same feeling that he too is being persecuted in some way. When a prospective client declines his plans in favor of those of a competitor, he feels that he has been personally insulted. To his friends he complains and protests against the way he is treated, and often he ends his whining remarks with: "Now tell me frankly, am I right or am I just no good?" Since neither alternative is correct, a direct answer is impossible. Any attempt at explanation is likewise impossible, for Harold promptly has his feelings hurt.

The tendency of the sensitive to read into every situation some reference to themselves, to make continually the impersonal into the personal, makes them unreasonable in their demands. Thus when Harold Johnson entertained a group of his friends at dinner their lack of appetites immediately became to him a matter of personal affront. If they did not drink freely of the wine he had provided, his remarks were in this vein: "You don't like my wine. You're not having a good time." The guests would then either drink the wine in spite of their disinclination, or give tacit admission to the fact that they were not enjoying themselves.

Helen McClintock, instead of expressing the resentment that springs from her sensitivity in a whining querulousness, as does Harold Johnson, takes refuge in haughtiness. Her characteristic exclamations are: "You should not have said that to me! How dare you do that to me? You should have more consideration for me!" Then with her head held high and back stiff, and with her mouth in a rigid line she retreats from the affront. But few of her associates recognize her majestic departure as a retreat. Her haughtiness gives to it an almost triumphant note that leaves her bewildered adversary crushed and humbled.

Helen McClintock is looked upon as having a strong and determined personality, a veritable tower of strength. She appears as a woman who enforces the most rigid principles for her conduct. In reality she has a weak personality; it is weak in ego. Her apparent strength of will arises merely from the manifestations of her sensitivity. Both her haughtiness and her persistence in clinging to past experiences, her dogged insistence in bearing a grudge—for that in reality is all that her apparent determination amounts to—are products of her sensitivity.

Helen McClintock has never married. She never will. But to the end of her life she will carry on and act out the tragedy of her one brief romance. It occurred forty-one years ago, but of that fatal night every incident is as clear in her memory as if it had occurred only yesterday. Every minute incident! To anyone of normal ego the whole affair was, indeed, minute, worthy of a passing pang, no more.

She had been nearly engaged to marry Charles Collins. For months, until the fateful night, he had played the humble and devoted swain so diligently that even her mistrustful scrutiny had sensed no flaw.

Charles had taken Helen to a dance. Carefully he had filled out her dance card for her. He had gently guided her through the first waltz. He had led her to her seat and bowed and fawned over her. She was soon to realize the hypocrisy of his every move. He mocked her—her, Helen McClintock!

When the violins sounded for the next dance, Charles had bowed and left her to claim his partner. Her partner for the dance would come and claim her. She sat in serene dignity, ready to smile at his approach, ready to rise gracefully and rest her hand lightly, very lightly, on his arm.

But he did not come.

Helen was left sitting alone, while Charles danced. She stiffened with the tragedy of it. She was left sitting alone.

Charles hurried to her side as soon as the dance was over. Her embarrassing plight was through no fault of his, but he bore the full blame for it. He bore also the crushing weight of her haughtiness.

Helen stalked from the danceroom. Charles followed, expostulating in vain. She remembered his words—every word. He had said that if she left he must go with her, and that when he left, his partners would be placed in the same humiliating position in which she had been placed. And she remembered the stern justice of her own brief reply. She had told him that if he thought more of them than of her he could remain. That in fact she had no desire for his company. Charles had insisted tearfully that it was not his fault that she had been neglected. And well she remembered her reply, "It might just as well have been you." Those were the last words she had ever spoken to him. When that night she had

shut the front door of the house she had shut Charles
out of her life.

But she clung to the memory; she built onto it; she
amplified it. For forty-one years her whole life has re-
volved about it. In these years she has taken no part in
any social activities. They remind her of the dance.
She has not gone to church. A church reminds her of
marriage. She does not approve of marriage.

All of the townspeople know that there has been
some great tragedy in Helen's life. None remembers
the actual details, but most believe that her lover was
killed on their wedding day. Everyone treats Helen with
the gentle consideration due to one who, strong in her
principles, has devoted her whole life to the memory
of a great tragedy. It is thus that Helen wishes to be
treated.

And Charles? He moved from town forty years ago;
he is married. He is oblivious to the part he plays in
Helen's "tragedy." In fact, he has forgotten Helen.

The sort of married life that Charles fortunately
escaped when Helen spurned him may be inferred from
that of Helen's sister Martha. She, like Helen, is sensitive and haughty. She lives with her husband, but she
does not speak to him for months at a time. All remarks
then intended for him are directed to the maid. In his

presence she will say: "Sarah, tell Mr. Gardener that I shall expect him at six this evening. I am having guests."

And they are always Mrs. Gardener's guests. She does not entertain her husband's friends.

William Gardener tolerates the situation more from habit than for any other reason. He has long since given up hope of any reconciliation. In fact, he can't remember now what the cause of their disagreement was. His interests are in his business, his golf, and his clubs. He stays away from home as much as possible.

He rarely thinks of his marital situation any more, but not so Martha. She is continually suspicious of her husband, certain that he is deceiving her with other women. When he says he is leaving town on a business trip, she invariably telephones to his office and his clubs and often to cafés as well. She gives no name, merely asks if Mr. Gardener is there. She has always been told that he isn't, but she is certain in her own mind that he has ordered his secretary and bribed the stewards to say he is not there. Twice she has employed detectives to follow him on his business trips. The detectives have reported nothing to confirm her suspicions. She has no doubt her husband has bribed them.

There are elements in the attitude and behavior of the sensitive that are strongly suggestive of the mental illness known as paranoia. Indeed, many of the sensitive, without being mentally ill, are distinctly paranoid in their tendencies. In paranoia there is the same mistrust of others, the same tenacity of memory for affronts, the same ideas of self-reference, and the same feeling of persecution. But in paranoia these features are exaggerated. There may even be developed elaborately systematized delusions of persecution.

The man with paranoia, like the one who is merely sensitive, usually tries at first to escape from his imagined persecution, to flee from his persecutors. But the wounded feelings of the sensitive and the absurd beliefs of the man with paranoia have an emotional origin. They are based upon a sensation. One cannot run away from one's own emotions. The feeling of persecution persists. Finding no relief in hiding, the man with paranoia attempts to defend himself against those whom he has decided are his persecutors. Finding no relief in this defense, he may become aggressive, sometimes violently aggressive. But all this time, like the sensitive man, it is his own sensation that deceives him. He is fleeing from and fighting against a projection of his own emotions.

Some of those who suffer from paranoia are the most dangerously violent of the mentally ill, but most are mere pathetic "cranks" who write interminable letters to prominent citizens and statesmen, seeking aid in obtaining protection against their "enemies." And often these "enemies," whose malign influence those with paranoia sense at every turn of their daily lives are situated in quarters indeed flatteringly high. There can be self-aggrandizement even in persecution.

Thus one poor soul with paranoia lived out to the best of his feeble ability the belief that he was the rightful heir to the British throne, that those who posed as the royal family had conspired to deprive him of his heritage. He could by a sort of genealogical legerdemain give proof of his claim. But the greatest proof was the fact that the family feared him. He knew they feared him, because they sent their hirelings to spy upon him and threaten him. When he saw a man on the street, that man was a spy. When he saw two men talking together, it was obvious that they were talking about him, plotting against him. When he heard the city clock strike midnight, it was a signal that his enemies had arranged between them to tell of his whereabouts. He even bragged a little of his cleverness in besting his persecutors. He was driving his car along a wide state road (paranoia does not, at least in its early stages, interfere with such abilities) when suddenly many cars surrounded his. There were cars in front of him and cars behind him. These cars held his enemies. But he outwitted them. He turned quickly into a side road and they, apparently oblivious to his escape, stayed on the main highway.

The absurdity of his behavior marks him as irrational. But only in degree does it differ from that described for the men and women whom we have classed as sensitive: Margaret Holman, who saw insult in a gesture; the Reverend Doctor Chester, who found persecution in the words of a schoolboy; Harold Johnson, who sensed self-reference in the appetites of his guests; Helen McClintock, who found a persecuting tragedy in the commonplace; and Martha Gardener, who was obsessed with the idea that her husband deceived her.

Each had a different way of acting out, rationalizing, in their separate lives, the sensation they experienced from their sensitivity. Sensitivity does not dictate the rôle that behavior shall assume. It simply provides the sensation that is the basis of the behavior. The rôle itself, the way the sensation is acted out, is determined wholly by psychological mechanism working in the field of character formation. And ego weakness not only in the form of sensitivity, but in all of its forms shows an exaggerated response to the mechanism that yields peculiarities of behavior, mechanisms such as repression, compensation, sublimation, regression, projection. These mechanisms have been investigated by several important schools—the Freudian, the Adelerian, the Jungian. But to follow out such avenues leads at once into fields beyond the scope and purpose of this book.

It has been our aim to deal only with the basic qualities upon which the mechanisms of character formation are superimposed. We deal with the foundations of personality endowed in the flesh—physique, intelligence, temperament, ego—and impulse.

PART VI

THE STREAMS OF LIFE

Chapter VIII

THE STREAMS OF LIFE

IMPULSE is the energizing element, the driving force of personality.

To such an element only the broadest and most general definition can be given: impulse is the sum-total of all of the biological urges that seek their satisfaction in the environment.

Every human desire, purpose, hope, and action is energized by impulse. It is from impulse that all other components of personality are vivified. Temperament, intelligence, ego, can color, shape, and modify the streams of impulse-life that pass through them toward the environment, but they can originate no forces. Force lies only in impulse.

Impulse, like life itself, is simple, primitive, crude in its fundamental qualities. Complexity lies only in the expression given to impulse by the other elements of personality. Impulse itself has only strength and direction—direction toward broad goals in which lie the sources of satisfaction for the biological needs. The impulse-life of a human being differs in no particular from that of the brute beasts; they have the same general needs and the same general sources of satisfaction as man. Man derives the human qualities of his personality from the modification given to impulse by his temperament, his ego, his intelligence and finally by his formed character.

From the manifestations of impulse we know that in each man impulses, when aroused, flow outward toward the environment through inherent channels which lead in the direction of the general sources of satisfaction for separate biological needs. The number and precise direction of these channels are matters of debate and definition. But in the broadest consideration two are beyond dispute—the one that carries the stream of impulse-life directed toward preservation of self and the one that carries the stream of impulse-life directed toward preservation of the species. In the simplest and most obvious forms in which impulses in these two broad streams are manifested, they are seen as those toward food and those toward sex.

But the stream of impulse-life directed toward preservation of self is not limited to a demand for food. Its scope is broader, including all needs and purposes

which have as their ends the maintenance of the entity
of the individual—not only the corporal entity, but also
the entity of the personality—self-protection, self-
development, and all self-interests. Likewise the stream
of impulse-life directed toward preservation of the
species extends in scope far beyond its most direct and
most immediate expression in sexual activity. It extends
to all needs and purposes which have as their ends the
maintenance of the entity of human society—all human
relations.

Below these broad channels that lead the impulses to
the surface is the great well of impulse-life itself. When
aroused it can be made to flow into one channel or another. But the inherent direction given to it points, as
we have said, only toward the general nature of the goals
in which satisfaction can be achieved. The specific goals
and objects from which the gratification is derived are
largely a matter of character formation.

Character thus becomes the ultimate directive influence to the impulses and hence to the personality as a
whole. But character is not inborn; it is acquired. And
in its acquisition the character for each individual must,
of necessity, be shaped about those qualities of personality with which he is endowed. Character when formed
designates the specific sources of satisfaction for the

impulse and likewise the specific situations—the stimuli —which shall arouse the impulse. But character does not, and cannot, affect the strength of the impulse or alter its fundamental direction. Acquired character determines what sort of food hunger finds agreeable—or disagreeable—and what sort of sex experiences give satisfaction—or dissatisfaction—to sex desire. But character does not originate hunger or sex desire nor can character be so formed as to supply goals that will satisfy hunger with sex experience or satisfy sex desire with food.

In dealing with the structure of personality from the analytical approach our start has, of necessity, been with behavior and our conclusion with impulse. We have worked inward. If our approach had been that of synthesis we should have started with impulse and traced its radiations outward through personality into formed character, and followed them finally to their specific goals in the environment. We then should have concluded with behavior. Such a course would have paralleled that of evolution, the gradual development of a personality which at each stage of added complexity approached nearer and nearer to the human.

If, robot like, we were to build a personality out of the material of living things, we should take first the vital element, impulse—the nucleus of all personalities from the highest to the lowest. Next we should incorporate this impulse in a physique, and since we deal with man, a human physique. We should then have an individual, but not a human being. It would be a creature only of desires and strength and physical form.

Next we should add temperament, surround the impulse with moods and emotions that would regulate its speed, its excitability, and color its display. As final additions there would be ego to give consciousness of self and intelligence to give consciousness of decision.

We should then have a human-like personality, but still it would be in robot form. If it were truly human, it would be far more complex than we have made it, for no element would stand alone, simple in its addition. Instead every part would be woven into the whole in a vast elaboration of interplay and interdependence. The personality would not then be a composite such as we have represented it. It would be an entity. It would be a human personality with all its inborn qualities, but not yet a man with determined behavior and specific goal for the satisfaction of the impulses that seethe out toward the environment. Instead we should have a huge baby, a personality undirected in behavior, inexperienced, unconditioned. But it would be a personality with definite individuality, an individuality given to it by the qualities of the element with which it was endowed.

Placed in an environment in which its impulses must seek their sources of satisfaction, a character would gradually be acquired by this personality—a character adapted not to impulse in its basic form, but to impulse modified by the particular endowment of temperament, ego, and intelligence. It is the conditioning of the inherent emotional qualities surrounding the impulse that leads to the designation of the specific sources of satisfaction and likewise the designation of the specific stimuli which shall arouse the impulse.

Thus babies are born with a desire for food, but they are not born with a desire to satisfy this hunger with the assortment of foods that adults find agreeable. The baby in growing up learns by experience to like some and dislike others of the vast array of edibles consumed by human beings. This finding of sources of satisfaction, and also of dissatisfaction, for hunger is not merely a matter of cultivating the palates; it involves the conditioning of the entire field of emotions—it involves character formation. When thus conditioned, the impulses directed toward food have become surrounded with emotional qualities. These qualities dictate the specific objects in which appetite may achieve satisfaction.

The Chinese child learns to like rice cooked in castor oil; he learns to like it because the adults surrounding him have learned to like it. They express their liking for it. Surrounding this oil, so distasteful to many Occidentals, there is an enormous number of factors affecting the emotions of the child. Surrounding it are the sense of home and security, the love for the mother and father, the desire to please them by eating, the impression made by the mother's facial expression as she offers the dish, and so on through a multitude of factors affecting the emotions of the particular child in relation to the food. The child by this conditioning finds for the impulse toward food a source of satisfaction surrounded by an agreeable emotional coloring. But it could as readily have developed a disagreeable coloring and correspondingly a distaste—indeed an intense aversion—for the food. The sight or smell of the oil brings back to the child the same feeling and hunger or aversion is aroused.

The ease with which the child could be led to like or dislike the food—and indeed which of the two, like or dislike, shall develop—would depend upon the personality of the child as much as upon the environment. The critical feature would not be the environment, but the impression made upon the child by the environment—

the interpretation given to the environment by the child. And this interpretation would be influenced by the inherent individual qualities of the child's personality.

The child with the well-balanced personality is adaptable to a wide range of environmental situations. It is easily guided. The child of less-well-balanced personality is correspondingly less adaptable. For it, character formation is more difficult and good character formation far more important. Character formation offers the only possible compensating influence for abnormality in personality.

The cultivation of tastes for food is one of the simplest examples of conditioning toward character formation. Hunger is direct—food to man—and does not involve the complicated relations of one individual to another as does the stream of impulses directed toward preservation of the species. It is in this field of human relations that the impulses have their greatest difficulty in finding agreeable objects of satisfaction and in which the objects are the most diverse. And it is in this field also that the strength of impulse and the peculiarities and deviations of impulse show most strikingly.

Although the basic biological needs of all men are the same in their general nature, it does not follow that in different men the strength of the demand for these needs is the same. The source of the impulse-life, the wellspring itself, may vary in its volume and hence, in the strength with which it pushes outward through its channels. Some men are born to have a stronger impulse-life than other men. Moreover, the strength of impulses varies in the individual not only with the phases of physical development from infancy to maturity and from maturity to senescence, but also with the conditions of life. During illness and fatigue, hunger and sex desire—indeed desire for all social participation—diminish. They return to their normal strength with health and rest. The excessive use of drugs, such as alcohol, tobacco, and the narcotics, may greatly diminish the strength of impulse.

Strength of impulse-life is closely related to physical vigor and stamina. Men with strong impulse are more vigorous and more aggressive than men with weak impulse. But success, even in competitive endeavors, is not wholly a matter of strong impulse, of aggression. Intelligence and temperament each play an important part and so also does formed character. But none of these features alters the aggression; they merely modify and direct its display. And none can supply or take the place of aggression. A man of high intelligence, of talent, even though his impulses are weak, may be strikingly successful in certain walks of life—and equally be doomed to failure in others. The artist or the writer or the philosopher working alone in no actual personal competition with other men may, in spite of feebleness, meekness, and lack of aggression, be a great artist, or a great author, or a great philosopher from sheer intellectual and artistic brilliancy. Equally such a man might be a pathetic failure in all endeavors requiring aggression. On the other hand, the business man of strong impulse-life, but of low intelligence, may, in spite of his vigor, fail because of his stupidity. And again the man of strong impulse but with poor direction from character formation may dissipate his energy so diffusely that his aggression leads to no end of social productivity. The fact remains, however, that in a competitive society the rewards of life are mainly for those of strong impulses—for the aggressive.

There is no direct way in which strength of impulse-life can be determined infallibly. It is revealed only in total behavior. But there may be clues that indicate at least the general strength. We have in previous chapters pointed out an association between strength of impulse and certain peculiarities of temperament and ego. Temperament and ego cannot of themselves give vigor and aggression to personality; those vital qualities are to be found only in impulse-life itself. But certain features of temperament and ego depend for their peculiarity upon the strength or weakness of the impulse-life that actuates them.

Thus a true explosive temperament is dependent upon and therefore indicative of a strong impulse. The same applies, but in somewhat less degree, to vivacity and irritability. Men weak in impulse do not show the aggressiveness inherent in true irritability; at most they exhibit a querulous resentment and temper tantrums.

The cheerful and the indifferent moods can exist with any strength of impulse, but the gloomy and anxious moods are far more often associated with weak than with strong impulses.

Peculiarities of ego yield perhaps the clearest insight into the strength of the impulse-life that lies behind them. The true egoist, and also usually the egocentric, have strong impulses. The weak of ego—the submissive, the resentful, the sensitive—have in turn, weak impulses.

If impulse-life flowed directly to its most obvious goals, it would be simple to estimate its strength from the demands of sex. But the situation is complicated by manifestations arising from character formation. Indirect goals can be established for the impulse toward sex.

[313]

It may be forced into obscure quarters by attempts at suppression. And finally, its lack may even be disguised.

When conditioned by character formation, the impulse which would otherwise be directed toward sex can be made to achieve at least partial satisfaction in objects that are seemingly remote from sex itself. The wellspring of impulse may thus be tapped and drawn upon to supply the driving force for efforts which, if productive, are certainly not reproductive. To this diversion of impulse the term sublimation is applied. The man who plays tennis, or swims, or writes a play, or does his job in the world to the best of his ability, carries out these endeavors on energy supplied from the general source of all impulse-life. As a result he has less energy to direct toward the more specific goals of sex and less desire in this direction.

There are some men of exceptional strength of impulse whose abundant energy supplies the driving force for a multitude of productive—and unproductive—activities. They are towers of strength in whatever walk of life they follow, whether it be high or low: the aggressive financier of wide activity, the athlete of ferocious stamina, the indefatigable soldier, the insatiable monster of depravity. Such men, when their activities are productive, are often held up as examples for emulation—a fallacy upon which we have already commented. Few men are so fortunately endowed with strength of impulse that they possess their superabundance of vitality.

Most, indeed, can successfully accomplish the tasks before them only by conservation of impulse-life—the avoidance of dissipation of impulse. By this conservation, the restriction of impulse to a limited range of goals, the man of moderate strength of impulse may become highly productive. Without this singleness of purpose his energies are often insufficient to carry him to any height of success. For an illustration of this phase of the subject, the reader is referred to the case given on page 119. The limitation imposed by moderate intelligence was the point primarily stressed there, but a contrast is made also between the influence of great and moderate strength of impulse in shaping careers.

Impulse-life can be sublimated, but it cannot be successfully suppressed. If the channels for its outlet are blocked, the impulse will cut to the surface and break forth in strange and unexpected places. Some of the most devious traits of human behavior arise from attempts to suppress impulse-life instead of providing satisfactory—sublimated if need be—goals for its outlet.

The Puritan, in forcing himself to avoid all thoughts

of sex, has not abolished his impulse toward sex. It often finds its outlet in an aggressive morality, a desire to chastise the spirit—and even the flesh—and to force and bend others to his views. Such excessive morality, especially when combined with mental or physical punishment of self or others, is essentially a sex perversion.

But the Puritan does not always have strong impulses held in restraint. He may have weak impulses that require little effort to restrain them. The ascetic who has denounced all aggression and all manifestations of his biological desires may be a strong man with restraint (if he is, he will suffer the torments that St. Anthony experienced), but far oftener he is a weak man who in his asceticism is merely making a virtue of necessity.

The glutton who gorges himself may have a weaker impulse than the man of restrained habits of eating. The individual aggressive in social situations may merely lack the restraint of good manners. The lascivious man, whose interests appear to center continually about matters of sex, may have weaker impulses in this direction than the Puritan who forces himself to avoid thoughts of sex. It is equally true that the lascivious man's emphasis upon sex may arise from the pressure of a strong impulse-life. But it may arise also from the fact that his character formation has included few goals for an im-

pulse of only moderate strength, that he has few productive, sublimated interests into which his impulses may
be diverted; they are therefore concentrated on sex. Or
again, the reason that sexual matters are foremost in his
thoughts, the reason that he brings some gesture toward
sex into every social relation with women, may be because he is worried over the fact that in reality his impulses are weak. His lasciviousness may be merely
braggery, a defense mechanism.

Within the past two decades much study has been
given to the peculiarities of the impulse toward sex;
many books have been written concerning sex, indeed
whole philosophies of human behavior have been built
about it. This emphasis upon sexual matters has had a
highly beneficial effect in so far as it has tended to correct the ignorance and purposeful slighting of sex that
marked the Victorian period. But the movement has not
been stopped at this desirable end; instead it has been
carried to the point where definitely there is danger of
overvaluing the importance of sex in a rational understanding of human nature and human relations.

Part at least of the overemphasis is due to a confusion
of terms. If by sex there is meant the entire stream of
impulse-life directed toward preservation of the species,
then there can be no doubt of the overwhelming impor-

tance of "sex" in all human relations. But if sex signifies merely those matters that are specifically correlated with reproductive functions—and this is unquestionably the light in which most members of the laity regard the term—then it does not occupy a paramount position in all human activities.

The fact is that for the man or woman with a well-balanced personality and a well-formed character, sex, in the sense of reproductive activities, occupies no over-whelming part of attention. There may be frequent sexual relations or none, but sex, to such an individual, is a part and parcel of life given its rational place and not constantly elevated to a position of prominence. On the other hand, sex may, and often does, become a dominating feature both of thought and behavior when there is weakness, deviation, or immaturity in the impulse-life or when character has not been well formed.

Hunger is as strong a biological urge as is sex desire. But it is not only the starving man whose thoughts center on food. The same is true also of the man of fickle appetite, the dyspeptic, the gourmet, and the gourmand. For the man of healthy digestion and well-directed appetite, thoughts of food do not constantly occupy his attention. But the dyspeptic finds no satisfaction even in an abundance of food. Similarly, the individual with some peculiarity in the sexual component of his impulse-life, or who has an illy-formed character, may not be able to view sex in a rational light. It is he and not the average and more normal man whose mind is continually filled with thoughts of sex and who shows the peculiarities of sexual behavior. It is from the psychological study of such deviated individuals that has arisen the belief that sex is the dominating factor in all human relations. It is to such men. But the conclusion cannot be drawn that it is to all men.

The impulses directed toward sexual goals show a progressive change in both strength and direction that is correlated with the physical development of the reproductive functions. The child, immature in these functions, has feeble impulses toward sex; they are diffuse and inherently undirected. They are experienced merely as a vague restlessness that may be soothed by the motion of rocking or by stroking the skin, or by contact with the mother's body. At most, they arouse in the child a desire to explore its body, to stroke and pat its own skin, perhaps to suck its fingers.

With each year of childhood the impulses toward sex grow stronger, but they still retain their diffuse form. So slow is the development that the child adjusts readily to the gradual changes. Not until puberty does a critical period arrive. Influenced then by a greatly heightened activity of glands of internal secretion, the functional activity of the reproductive organs is established. The impulses toward sex increase in strength abruptly. For a time they may dominate the entire impulse-life. Under their influence personality is modified, altered. The boy and girl suddenly find that they are different—actually different persons from those they were only a few months before. The adjustments that they have made to their environment no longer suffice for the needs of their impulses. New ones must be made to provide outlets. New goals of satisfaction must be sought. A new phase of character must be formed. This is a stormy period in the lives of many young people, a time of bewilderment, uncertainty, and emotional disturbances. But in their dilemma some guidance is given to them by their own impulse-life.

At this time the impulses toward sex develop normally an inherent direction toward the opposite sex. Boys of this age do not need instruction to bring their interest toward girls; nor girls toward boys. It arises spontaneously. The hoyden loses her carefree ways and develops a shyness toward boys. And the boy who has avoided girls because they are a "nuisance" suddenly exhibits a shamefaced desire to be near them.

At puberty the impulse toward sex is not fully established in strength. Neither has it lost all of its diffuseness. It is still immature, still infusing the vague restlessness that marked its earlier stages. And this same restlessness can be experienced even by those who are adult and in whom the goals of the impulse are well established. The restlessness develops then when the attainment of the goals is denied. The child at puberty has the restlessness, but without the capabilities of attaining a valid satisfaction. His efforts toward relief often take the direction of playing at sex—puerile courtships, first toward one partner and then abruptly toward another and with utter disregard to the fitness of any. Frequently the object of affection is some far older woman, one of his school-teachers, or even a married aunt. And all these courtships are marked with unreasonable jealousies and covered with needless secrecies— "puppy love." Often, too, the sex-play extends to include physical contact, the accessories of more mature sexual goals such as kissing and hugging—"petting."

In the years immediately following puberty, the impulses toward sex normally continue to increase in strength, but at a slower rate. Adjustments then become easier. The courtships of this period are on a more aggressive and rational basis. They show a far greater constancy. Definite and valid goals are being shaped. Restlessness still persists and is often exhibited in hectic participation in dances and parties—interests that usually decline rapidly following marriage, provided that valid sexual relations are established.

But at no time, either before or after marriage, can the playing at sex, courtship, serve as a valid goal for those of normal strength of impulse and rarely so even to those of weak impulse. The accessories of mature sexual goals are experienced and recognized as incomplete. The girl fondled by her *fiancé* often loses admiration for him as a man. She does not reason out the steps by which she reaches this conclusion; she merely senses a lack of satisfaction. She, and this is true of the boy as well, may in consequence become irritable, unreasonable, nagging, jealous, and not infrequently acutely anxious. The particular reaction will, of course, depend upon the temperamental endowment of the individual. Those with the anxious mood are particularly prone to such emotional disturbances and from them may develop typical anxiety crises.

The fondling that may occur in long courtships is of itself a form of conditioning toward character formation in sexual relations. Pseudo goals of gratification— but never valid ones—may in time be acquired by this type of conditioning. In subsequent marital relations prolonged reëducation—reconditioning—may thus be required to overcome these habits and to allow the development of satisfactory and satisfying goals, which indeed may never be attained. The difficulties placed in the way of arriving at these mature goals because of poor or perverse character formation in sexual matters is a common source of personality disturbance.

Guidance in character formation thus becomes a matter of great importance in avoiding such disturbances. But in the society of today serious difficulties are imposed upon the establishment of valid goals in sexual relations. The impressions made in youth, particularly in the formative period following puberty, are especially strong in their guiding influence. And it is at this period that youth faces a conflicting situation. He—and she as well—is surrounded on every side by influences that tend to stimulate and arouse sexual desire, but which do not provide education either as experience or instruction to dispel the misconceptions that invariably surround sex. Plays, moving pictures, magazines, novels, and indeed social conversation frequently center their themes about sexual excitation. The fashion in feminine dress is often deliberately provocative. The emotions and the imagination are appealed to, but not the intelligence. The psychological accessories of sexual relations are exposed and emphasized into a false importance in the mind of the inexperienced youth. The youth may in consequence develop an apparent sophistication in sexual matters, talk glibly of them, even symbolically, but at the same time hold entirely erroneous views toward the most fundamental physiological facts of sexual relations.

Moreover many of the youths of today are really not youths. Physical sexual maturity is reached by the eighteenth or nineteenth year in the male, and by the fifteenth or sixteenth year in the female. They are then men and women, but under the existing economic and educational systems they are regarded and treated as children, particularly in the so-called upper social levels. Marriage rarely takes place now at the age of sexual maturity. Youth is accordingly artificially prolonged through college years and into early business or professional life to a possible detriment of good character formation in sexual matters.

For the individual of well-balanced personality with great or normal strength of impulse, the handicaps imposed by society are not insurmountable. For such an individual—as we have repeatedly emphasized—character formation is flexible; he is adaptable. The normal relations of human society were founded to suit the personality of such an individual. His approach may be awkward and hesitant, but usually he eventually makes his way in safety through the maze imposed by conventions and prudery. The very strength of his impulse, his inherent ability to recognize true and false goals, guides him in reasonable safety.

But for the youth of weak impulse—a weakness frequently associated with deviation in ego and temperament—the obstacles placed in the way of proper character formation in sexual matters are, unless assistance is given, often insurmountable. Education in sexual matters—particularly toward the avoidance of false information—is of great benefit to the normal youth, but it is literally indispensable to the one of weak impulse. It is he in whom the great majority of the personality disturbances associated with sex occur. And many—perhaps the majority—could be avoided by careful education. It is in this matter of sexual education that modern civilization, for all its apparent advancement, falls far behind the savage community. The savage may not be taught to read or write; he may never be instructed in the æsthetic aspects of a higher life; but he learns the fundamental biological relations of man and woman early and normally.

The individual of weak impulse can, by proper and early education, be guided toward valid goals for his sexual impulses and thus assisted in avoiding personality disturbances. But there are other individuals in whom education cannot achieve this desirable end. They are specifically those in whom there is a definite inherent deviation in the direction of the sexual impulse and also those in whom the sexual impulse fails to attain maturity and remains throughout life in the form in which it exists at puberty. Little or nothing can be done to correct such abnormalities. When, however, they are fully recognized and thoroughly understood by the individual, much can be done to control and relieve their manifestations by deliberate attempts at character formation. The personality disturbances toward which such deviations tend may thus in part be avoided.

The most serious derangement of impulse life is that of inherent deviation in the direction of sexual impulse toward the same rather than the opposite sex. The genesis of this deviation usually lies in peculiarities of physical and psychological development.

On the basis of anatomical differences we are accustomed to classify all human beings into two definite and completely opposite groups—men and women. But psychologically—even biologically—there are no valid grounds for this dogmatic separation.

If individuals were examined in their totality both of physique and personality we should find that no man is wholly male and no woman wholly female. And this fact applies to the anatomical structure even of those organs upon which the sweeping separation into two completely opposite sexual groups is made. In the genital tract of the most normal male there is a vestige, an anatomical remnant, of the female reproductive system. Also in the body of a woman there are normally vestiges of organs that are developed to functional activity only in the male.

In the early embryonic state the male and female alike have the same rudimentary genital organs. Sex cannot be differentiated by any external evidence. The sole difference between the two lies in an hereditary endowment carried in the minute genes of the cells. In time this genetic element exercises its influence on the glands of internal secretion. They in turn through products formed and poured into the blood of the embryo cause one or the other portions of the until then undifferentiated sexual organs to develop. The remainders remain rudimentary. Thus the child is born male or female according to which of the organs has achieved growth.

But even at birth sexual differentiation, in spite of the anatomical dissimilarity, is far from complete. The baby boy and girl do not possess those differences in physique and personality which in later life give a fuller differentiation of sex.

At the time of puberty a second stage of glandular activity comes into play. In response, the so-called secondary sexual characteristics develop. Growth is affected; definite differences appear in the configuration of the male and female physiques. The growth of the skeleton is modified, as is also the deposition of fat with the development of the broader hips and the rounder figure of the female. In the male the larynx widens, the voice deepens, and the beard develops.

Any one of these qualities could be taken as the basis for sexual differentiation quite as logically as the anatomical configuration of the reproductive organs. The development of both depends upon precisely the same basic internal influences. But the fact remains that there are some women whose voices are deeper than those of some men, there are women who develop beards, and there are women who have physiques that appear more muscular and more masculine than those of some men.

[328]

If sexual differentiation were made upon the basis of the secondary sexual characteristics there would be many exceptions to the usual differentiation and many uncertainties.

The anatomical form of the reproductive organs is determined with finality during a brief period of the early stage of development. There are rarely intermediate phases. The secondary sexual characteristics, on the contrary, are developed slowly and at a much later period. Their appearance depends upon the continuing activity of glands of internal secretion, an action exercised over many years. There is about them no finality; there are many deviations from the complete stages of differentiation. Consequently, in sexual determination made on the basis of the total physique there are some men who are more masculine than others and some women more feminine than others. The extremes in these groups overlap. There are some women more masculine than some men and some men more feminine than some women.

These features do not stop with the physique; they extend into the whole of the personality. The direction given to the sexual impulse depends in its development upon the same influences as those which are responsible for the appearance of the secondary sexual characteristics; in fact, it is one of the secondary sexual characteristics. Consequently, the direction given to the impulse may show variations similar to those appearing in physical traits. The impulse may in fact be inverted in direction so that the "male" body holds impulses directed toward the male sex and the "female" body impulses toward the female sex.

Although physical and psychological sexual differentiations are derived from a common influence, they may not of necessity both develop the same peculiarities. Women with distinctly masculine physiques, with a growth of hair on their faces, and even with deepened voices, may in every aspect of their personality be feminine. Likewise there are men who are soft of flesh, round of figure, and wide of hips, whose voices are shrill, but who are nevertheless virile and well directed in their impulse toward sex.

Frequently, however, some association does exist between the peculiarities of the physical traits and the direction of the impulses toward sex. Many males who have deviation in the direction of their impulses show definite feminine traits in their physique and also in their gestures.

A deviation in the direction of the sex impulse does not, however, invariably result in obvious sexual attraction for the same sex. The deviation may be slight and its import unrecognized by the individual. He may be capable of entering into physical sexual relations as a male, but he may nevertheless be rendered incapable of establishing definite and constant goals of sexual activity. He does not find satisfaction in his relations with those of the opposite sex. Consequently, if his impulse is strong, his behavior may be that of a Don Juan who seeks continually new sexual attachments as he flees from the incomplete satisfaction of the previous ones.

On the other hand, with less strength of impulse-life, but with an equal deviation in direction, many males remain simply bachelors. They show at no time strong attachments for women. Such feminine companions as they select are usually of no great strength of impulse-life. Such individuals are often, and generally unconsciously so, fond of the companionship of young men. This interest often leads them into the field of teaching in boys' schools and colleges or into work at the Y. M. C. A. or boys' clubs. Often these individuals exhibit a strong interest in æsthetic matters and a truly feminine orderliness in conducting their homes and social activities.

But not all males with an inversion of the sexual impulse remain bachelors. Many, recognizing their own deviation and fearing acutely that others will recognize it, deliberately marry to escape detection.

One of the cruelest tragedies of personality is that which may occur in the adolescent boy deviated in the direction of his impulses. He fails to feel the interests and the desires of his more normal companions. He experiences an affectionate and jealous interest toward other boys which is not returned by them. He senses a deficiency in himself, but usually he does not have insight into the cause. His is a devastating struggle.

Nor does the tragedy always end when he has finally achieved insight. He is faced then with the fact that through no fault of his own he has become for most men, and for most women as well, an object of contempt.

What he really deserves is compassion and help. And these kindly qualities toward him come with the understanding of the basis of the deviation in his personality.

Prejudices must play no part in the minds of those who would truly understand the personalities of others.

Of this fact we gave warning in our first chapter. No man, as we said there, can without bias judge the personality of another in its totality. Unbiased judgment of personality can be achieved only by an analysis in which the elements are separated and dealt with as abstractions. An unreasonable repugnance toward those with a deviation in the direction of their sex impulse may of itself arise from a similar defect—perhaps slight and unrecognized—in the personality of the observer. He is prejudiced by his desire to escape all association with the defect from which he himself suffers.

Immaturity of impulse, like deviation, is an inborn trait that cannot be remedied, although, as we have said, its effects may in part be compensated by character formation.

In some individuals the development of the sex impulses, for no known reason, is arrested at some stage short of maturity. These impulses, while they may grow in strength, fail to achieve the full inherent direction of normal development. They retain instead the diffuseness that marks the impulse-life of the young adolescent. Individuals with this immaturity of impulse may go on to actual sexual activity, but they are incapable of establishing valid and mature sexual goals. Instead they retain the vague restlessness and uncertainty that is typical of immaturity. And this immaturity shows in their personalities. Often it is expressed as a lack of direction in endeavor, an uncertainty of purpose in life, and as a tendency toward dilettantism rather than concentrated determined effort.

These are peculiarities which are exhibited by many boys and girls during the adolescent period. Such qualities are not abnormal at this time of life. They belong to this period and they are normally outgrown by the time physical maturity is attained. But those men and women in whom the impulses toward sex persist in immature form fail to reach maturity in personality; they "never grow up," but retain instead juvenile peculiarities throughout life.

Some even persist definitely in the juvenile sexual tendencies toward self, such as find expression in masturbation and narcissism. This latter peculiarity may at times be seen in an exaggerated interest in personal appearance arising not from a desire to impress others, but from an admiration of self. The boy who obtains a satisfaction in studying himself before the mirror, who flexes his muscles and turns his head for a better view of his features, is guilty of juvenile—and normal—narcissism. But equally normally this type of behavior is outgrown in the adult, but it may not be among adults who remain immature in impulse. Some women show a tendency toward narcissism in the gentle and pleasurable stroking of the gowns they are wearing and the elaborate—and public—care which they give to their facial "makeup" with lipstick and rouge. Some of the best customers of the "beauty specialists" are women with this narcissistic tendency; they find an exquisite pleasure in the ministrations given to their hair and flesh.

Immaturity of impulse, while influencing the behavior of the individual, does not dominate the entire personality and serve to identify it. Indeed, like strong or weak impulses, it may be associated with any one of a variety of temperamental qualities, with many degrees of ego strength, and with all levels of intelligence. It is of itself merely a part in a personality as a whole, and no personality can be defined by the peculiarities of only one of its elements.

Thus far in these chapters we have made no attempt to define a personality in its totality. Previously we have dealt only with the peculiarities of the individual elements. We have analyzed but not synthesized. In the opening chapter there was presented a basis of a structural analysis of personality. In subsequent chapters consideration was given to each of the genetic components defined there—physique, intelligence, temperament, ego, and impulse. But no one of these elements can alone constitute a personality. No human personality has only physique, or intelligence, or temperament, or ego, or impulse. Instead these elements, with their individual peculiarities, combine, each influencing all

[335]

others, to constitute the personality. Such a definition as intelligent personality, or a moody personality, lacks completeness; such designations as vivacious, explosive, or egocentric serve merely to mark predominant traits of personality. They do not of themselves reveal the personality as a whole.

No two personalities are precisely alike and there is, therefore, no short cut in the definition of personality. For each individual, physique, impulse, temperament, ego, and intelligence must be taken into consideration. But nevertheless there are certain combinations of qualities that may so dominate the personality as a whole as to allow a general definition. Such is the case with the so-called hysterical personality. It is dealt with here not only as an example of synthesis, but because its primary deviation is immaturity of impulse—immaturity of impulse combined in this case with definite peculiarities of ego and temperament.

The term hysterical is often loosely used and incorrectly applied to traits that belong wholly in the realm of temperament or character. Thus a woman with an uncontrolled, excitable temperament is sometimes referred to as hysterical; as is also one who, regardless of temperament, has had poor character formation and who is "spoiled" and shows temper tantrums.

The hysterical personality, as we deal with it here, results from the combination of immaturity in impulse, coldness of temperament (lack of resonance), and marked egocentricity. This combination of peculiarities so dominates the total personality as to dictate for it a definite type of reaction toward the environment.

The hysterical personality derives its primary peculiarity from a deviation in the element of impulse. But this immaturity of impulse does not alone result in the hysterical personality. If it did, every child and every adolescent would exhibit this type of personality. Neither does it derive its peculiarity from its coldness of temperament or its egocentricity. There are many cold egocentrics who are not hysterical. It is the domination derived from the influence of the combination of peculiarities that gives the hysterical personality its definite type of reaction toward the environment. This reaction is influenced, but its general nature never completely altered, by peculiarities that may occur in the remaining two components of personality—intelligence and physique.

The individual with the hysterical personality has only the guiding qualities of the youth at puberty—immature impulses. But he has the strong impulse and the mature physique of an adult. He has the selfishness that is given by lack of warmth, and he has the false goals of prestige that are given by egocentricity. He is a precocious child, a child with unpleasant qualities, playing a part in a world of grown-ups.

To such a man nothing is genuine; there is no genuineness in his personality. It is lacking in his impulse-life and lacking also in his ego. To him all life is a stage upon which he plays a rôle for the sake of prestige. He dramatizes, acts out every situation with himself in the leading rôle. His aim is prestige.

The lack of genuineness and also the immaturity show further in lying. Most individuals with hysterical personalities are inveterate liars. They lie over trifles; lie for effect; lie for the pure joy of lying. They lie maliciously to stir up trouble. Trouble makes excitement, and in the excitement they find new settings and new rôles for their dramatic efforts.

Again, the lack of genuineness and the immaturity show when the individual with a hysterical personality is confronted by a real demand and a real responsibility, as when the trouble he has stirred up is brought home to him. It is then that one of the most characteristic features of this personality may come into play: the responsibility is escaped by refuge taken in the symptoms of disease. But the peculiarities of the personality are

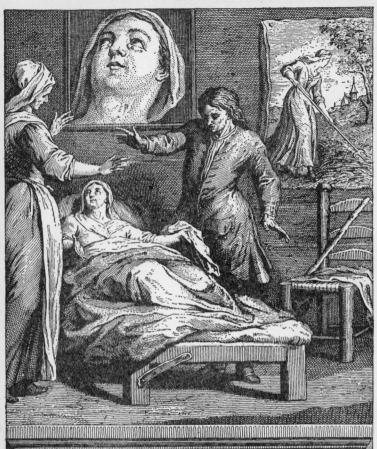

MARIE CARTERI

Est guerie le même jour 4. Septembre au Tombeau de Mr de PARIS, & toutes ses
douleurs cessent. Elle reconnoît le lendemain matin en ôtant son bandeau que les
grosseurs des fistules étoient infinim.^t diminuées, et qu'il ne restoit à ses yeux ni rou-
geur ni inflam.^on Au bout de 8. jours le peu de grosseur qui restoit au coin de ses yeux
disparoit entierem. Elle travaille dans les champs avec plus de force qu'elle n'avoit jamais fait.

carried even into this refuge. The normal man confronted by a disagreeable situation may not "feel well," the anxious man may have an anxiety-crisis, the psychoneurotic (but not hysterical) may have a stomach ache, or think he has cancer, but the hysterical individual does not stop at such thoughts or such minor manifestations. Even in portraying the symptoms of disease he continues to play a leading rôle. His illness has the appearance of a startling and grave disorder. A leg or arm, perhaps an entire side of his body, suddenly becomes paralyzed. Equally suddenly he may go blind. Again, he may lose his memory, forget his name, his home, and in amnesia wander away from the seat of his troubles. But rarely is the loss of memory so sudden that he fails to have time enough to remove all marks of identification from his clothes. He is a good dramatist, a consistent and thorough one. His acting is convincing. It even convinces him.

The rôles that the hysterical enact are on stages set in every social level. There are hysterical prostitutes and hysterical beggars. And there are also hysterical social leaders and hysterical multimillionaires. Each plays his part with a simplicity or complexity that is determined both by the degree of the personality deviation and by the environmental situation.

Thus in a simple setting the case of John Hoyt shows the typical use of disease as a refuge to escape responsibility. Hoyt was twenty-four. He was an athlete of some ability. And just previous to his difficulty he was ardently courting a young lady of well-balanced personality. She liked John. He was handsome, well dressed, amiable, amusing, and capable at sports. He played the ardent suitor gracefully, gallantly, almost too gallantly. The young lady sensed a certain lack of genuineness in his love-making. There was about it, so it seemed to her, a dramatic element which, although it might be flattering to some, appeared to her a trifle childish. Her interest in John stopped at mere liking. And so, to gain her love, John decided to dramatize a great event, to make himself the irresistible, virile hero.

He entered his name in a much-publicized amateur boxing competition. He began at once to train for the event, and from the training he squeezed every drop of dramatic effect. Other youths might do their road work on country lanes and wear soiled trunks and faded sweaters. But not so John! He chose the highroad and the city streets; his track shoes were polished; his trunks immaculately white, with vivid red stripes on the seams; his sweater was new and its color a delicate gray. As he ran, his automobile was driven after him. All in all it was a very impressive performance.

John would have been delighted to continue it indefinitely. But the time for the contest was nearing. It was only two days distant when he heard the disagreeable news. His name had been entered in the preliminaries with that of a contestant noted for his smashing fighting. One of John's friends advised him that his only chance of winning lay in standing up before grueling punishment and showing a superior endurance. This remark brought home to John the realities of the situation with appalling clarity.

He had given the actual contest little thought except in pleasing fantasies in which he saw himself standing in the squared ring, his arm held aloft to proclaim his victory, and the young lady of his fancy in the audience waving to him her frenzied approbation. But here was a reality that differed from his fantasy. He could not withdraw. He would have to fight; he would have to take punishment. And he might not win.

But he did not fight.

On the day of the contest it was regretfully announced by the judge that due to an unfortunate accident John Hoyt would be unable to participate. The accident had occurred on the last day of training and on

[343]

a busy thoroughfare. John had suddenly staggered and then stopped; he had thrust out his hands gropingly, feeling blindly for support. John had lost the sight of both eyes. He was rushed to the nearest hospital. The most careful examination failed to reveal the slightest defect that might account for his blindness. But there was no doubt of the blindness.

The young lady was sincerely sorry for the accident. She came to see John at the hospital. For her he dramatized his sorrow, his misfortune, his chagrin at the accident that had occurred when victory lay almost in his hands. If his sight had lasted only two days longer he would have been the champion. But in that possibility the young lady was not interested; she did not care for boxing or boxers, amateur or otherwise. John, carried away by his dramatic efforts, had failed to take into account this feature of the situation.

To the relief of his eye specialist and his family, John's sight was restored during the week following the boxing-contest.

The behavior of John Hoyt, while showing the typical childishness, lacked the more unpleasant traits exhibited by many individuals with the hysterical personality. A few brief episodes from the life of Mrs. Filmore Endicott will serve to illustrate their nature.

Before her marriage to Endicott, Margaret Courtwell had been known to her school and college mates as an inveterate liar and trouble-maker. On more than one occasion she had come under suspicion as the author of anonymous letters directed to the dean of the college, accusing her classmates of sexual offenses. She had gone to the dean in person, and in tears and with apparent unwillingness, but driven by a sense of duty—so she said had laid a formidable charge of attempted sexual assault against one of the younger male instructors of the college. Her story was dramatic, it was detailed, and it was graphic. The instructor was dismissed. There was in actuality no truth whatever in the accusation. Her malice was dictated wholly by the fact that she was in danger of failing the course taught by the instructor. But she had faced him before the dean and reiterated with every show of reluctance and modesty her story of the attempted assault.

No one had, or ever could, accuse Margaret of sexual irregularities. The men she chose for her friends were invariably weakly sexed. The other girls called them "sissies." Margaret's friendships with young men were platonic.

Filmore Endicott, whom she married, was thirty-eight years her senior. He was a prominent minister.

Into her married life she carried the same malicious trouble-making tendencies that had marked her college career. She attempted immediately to take charge of all the social activities of the church, to run everything. Finding her direct efforts opposed, she reverted to her tactics of lying, anonymous letters, and scandal-spreading. To the influential male members of the congregation she played the part of a coquette, attempting to win their support by a dramatic but restrained appeal of sex.

The previously peaceful congregation of the church literally writhed with the effect of the venom she had injected into it. Resignation after resignation came to Filmore Endicott from his parishioners. His suspicions were aroused toward his young wife. He questioned her. She promptly sued him for divorce, naming as corespondent the wife of the most socially prominent member of the congregation.

In court, her graceful leptosomic figure fashionably clad in black, she made a dramatic picture. She was the injured wife. She sought no revenge, no reparation, merely an opportunity to escape from a harrowing situation. Reluctantly—her voice broken by sobs—she told in the most minute and graphic detail the perverted sex relations of her husband with the corespondent. The judge who, in a long career had never heard a more frightful story, complimented her on her courage as he granted her the divorce.

Filmore committed suicide. The accused corespondent was divorced by her husband. Public opinion forced her to leave town.

In actual fact there was no single shred of truth in the story that Margaret Endicott dramatized in the courtroom. But she was a successful dramatist. She had a hysterical personality.

Character formation, as profound as its influence is in shaping the goals for the impulses, cannot compensate for the basic defects of the hysterical personality. Character cannot act as a substitute for maturity; neither can it supply genuineness to a personality in which none exists. The hysterical personality may be cultivated and polished; its possessors may develop social graces and charm. Margaret Endicott had these acquisitions. But even people with good manners and a knowledge of the conventions may lack genuineness; they may still retain all the qualities inherent in the hysterical personality, although their social training makes the display more subtle and more cautious and more dangerous than is the case when this training is lacking. When, however, there is insight—when the hysterical individual understands his own peculiarity—he can, by deliberate effort at character formation, learn to avoid the display of many of the more objectionable traits of this personality.

There are other combinations in the qualities of personality that in turn yield extreme types of personality as well defined as the hysterical—the eccentric, the active and "flabby" fanatical, the hypochondriacal, and so on. But such sharp definition is exceptional. Most men do not possess such striking combinations of peculiarities as to allow them to be classified as types.

This fact does not in the least prevent a description of their personalities. But they cannot be defined in single terms. Instead, a statement must be made setting forth the distinguishing qualities of each of the elements that unite to form personality. The combination, and only the combination, with the interrelation of all of the parts, designates the personality. The statement of this combination of qualities is the end result of the application of the method of structural analysis set forth in our opening chapter. Thus the statement, immature in impulse, cold in temperament, moderate or high or low in intelligence, leptosomic or pyknic in physique,

[348]

may be longer, but it is as definite in its descriptive result as is the corresponding term, hysterical personality.

In either case the structure of the personality is designated, its bare flesh revealed. And this is the raw material with all its ineradicable qualities which the operation of character formation must accept in shaping human behavior. Marvels of compensation for defect in the elements of personality can be accomplished by planned character formation. No man can change his personality, but he may alter his character. What is more, through his intelligent efforts he may assist others—particularly his children—in shaping their characters to productive ends, toward well-adjusted lives.

But the character desired cannot be forced upon the personality; it must be adapted and suited to it. Only unhappiness and discontent can follow attempts to force character formation in directions incompatible with the inherent elements of personality. Education must be suited to the child—not the child forced to suit the education. Self-improvement must be along lines to which the personality can adapt itself—not based merely on emulation.

Toward all efforts at planned character formation, all efforts at self-improvement, the first step must be an evaluation—a stock-taking—of the qualities with which the personality is endowed, the materials upon which the mechanisms of character formation are to be applied. And it is this structural revelation of personality that has been the sole purpose of this book—no further is its scope.

INDEX

Aggression, 21, 311-312
Alcohol, effects of on anxious, 207
    excitable, 160
    explosive, 172
    mood, 136
Anaemia, 39
Animals, torture of, 227
Anxiety, acute, 202, 341
    coitus interruptus, as cause of,
        206
    crisis. *See* anxiety, acute
    in diseases of the heart, 135
    symptoms of, 195-196, 201-203
    treatment of, 203
Anxious mood as basis of phobias,
        205-207
    psychoneuroses, 195-196, 202
    sexual impotency, 207-208
    description of, 195-208
    effects of alcohol on, 207
        coffee on, 207
        tobacco on, 207
    in courtship, 322
Aristotle, 3-4, 7-12, 16, 19-25, 28-29
Athletic physique and athletic
        prowess, 49
    description of, 46-47, 55
Athletics, 111
    explosiveness in, 164

Baldness, 45
Behavior, guided by character,
        13-14
    human, limits to, 88
    personality revealed by, 14

Beliefs, popular, fallacy of, 36
Bibliophiles, 71
Blood vessels, disease of, 39
Borgia, Cesare, 229
Bragging, 231, 242-244

Caesar, Julius, 249
Calvin, 71, 73-74
Cases, anxious mood, 197-201
    egocentric, destructive, 248-251
        juvenile, 233-234
        self-constructive, 245-246
    excitable, 154-159
    explosive, 162-171
    hypomanic, 61-62
    hysterical personality, 342-347
    irritable, 175-181
    low intelligence, 113-123
    phlegmatic, 183-186
    resentful, 271-283
    sensitive, 287-296
    torpid, 186-187
Cerebrum, 82
Character, 83, 85
    as read from face, 33
    definition of, 13, 89
    formation, 87-91
        and gloomy mood, 190
        at puberty, 320
        ease of, 309-310
        importance of, 93-94
        influence of environment on,
            88-89
        personality on, 91-95
    in goals for impulse, 305-311

Character formation—(*Continued*)
  in sexual relations, importance
    of, 323-324
  limits of, 94-96
  mechanism of, 308-311
  with weak impulse, difficulties
    to, 325-326
  influence of environment on,
    13-14
  reading, fallacies of, 33
  suited to personality, 349
"Characters" of Theophrastus, 3-4,
  7-12, 16, 19-25, 28, 29
  types of, 4
Charity, ostentatious, 246
Charlatan, 101
Charlemagne, 244
Cheerful mood, description of,
  188-189
Class employment, traditional, 124
Classification of personality, descriptive, 11-12
Cleopatra, 249
Cleveland, Grover, 71-72, 74
Coffee, influence of on mood, 136
Coitus interruptus, as cause of
  acute anxiety, 206
Collectors, 228
Comedians, 148
Compensation for deviation in
  personality, 98, 107-108, 349
Control of excitability, 154-160
  irritability, 177-181
Couthon, 97
"Cranks," 297-299
Criticism, 106-107, 240
  destructive, 248-251
  from gloomy mood, 190
  reaction of egocentrics to, 251-
    252
  sensitive to, 287-292
Critics, egocentrics as, 190
  gloomy as, 190

Cubist artists, 71
Cultist, 101

Day dreaming, adolescence, 68
Dementia, 64
Dementia praecox. *See* schizo-
  phrenia
Deviation in personality, compen-
  sation for, 98, 107-108, 349
Dilettantism, 333
Diseases of the heart, anxiety in,
  135
Distractiveness, 142
Dizziness, 201
Don Juan, 331
Don Quixote, 45
Dysplastic physique, 50-51

Education, 102-104, 111, 349
  definition of, 94
  fallacies of, 94-95
  in sexual matters, importance of,
    325-326
Ego, 24-25, 78, 91, 106, 108
  as an element of personality, 18
  definition of, 215
  evaluation of, 219-225
  goal in accomplishment, 218-221
    prestige, 220-221
  in relation to strength of im-
    pulse, 314-315
Egocentric, 25-30, 231-251
  as critics, 190
  constructive, 235-236
  definition of, 231-233
  destructive, 235-236, 247-251
  fields of endeavor, 239
  productive, 235-241
  reaction to criticism, 251-252
    flattery, 252
  self-constructive, 241-247
  youthful, 234
Egoism and bragging, 231
    torture of animals, 227

Egoist, criminal, 226-227
  description of, 25, 226-231
  in relation to self-consciousness, 268
Ego qualities, individuality of, 218
  strength, definition of, 215-217
    disturbance of during adolescence, 217-218
    evaluation of, 215-216, 257-258
    fluctuation of, 254-255
    influence of age on, 217-218
    weakness. See weak ego
    type of. See resentful, sensitive and submissive
Embarrassment, 156
Embryo, development of, 77-78
Emotive, 140
Emulation, fallacy of, 112-113, 121-122
Environment, influence of on character formation, 13, 14, 23, 88-89, 91
  of civilized community, 95
Etymology, medical, 42
Evolutionary development of personality, 77-89
Excitable, cases of, 154-159
  contrasted with explosive, 161
    normal man, 152
    vivacious, 151-152
  definition of, 140
  description of, 151-161
  effect of alcohol on, 160
    tobacco on, 160
  with anxious mood, 161
    irritable mood, 161
    low intelligence, 160-161
Excitability, control of, 154-160
  degree of, 139
Exophthalmic goiter, 139
Expansiveness, 142
Experimenters, 70
Explosive, cases of, 162-171
  contrasted with excitable, 161
    vivacious, 161

Explosive, cases of—(Continued)
  description of, 140, 161-172
  effects of alcohol on, 172
Explosiveness in athletics, 164
  control of, 167-172

Facial shapes, 42, 45-46, 49-51
Fallacies, popular, 36
Falstaff, Jack, 34, 45
Fanatics, 267, 348
Fantasy, 68
Fashion, influence on sexual selection, 55-56
Fickleness, 142
Flattery, egocentrics reaction to, 252
Food in relation to mood swings, 209
Franklin, Benjamin, 70-72, 74

Gallstones, 39
Genius, 103
Gloomy, as critics, 190, 193
  facial expression of, 194
  mood, 188
    and resonance, 193
    and sensitivity, 284
    description of, 189-194
    with irritability, 194
Goiter, exophthalmic, 139
Gossips, 243
Grant, Ulysses S., 70

Habitus apoplepticus, 38, 41
  phthysicus, 38, 40-41
Hamlet, 34
Heart, palpitation of, 102
Hereditary, 91-95, 117
Hippocrates, 38-40
Hitler, 97
Hobbies, 68
Hypomanic, 58-61
  case of, 61-62
  peculiarities of, 62-63

Hysterical personality, cases of, 342-347
  character formation in, 347-348
  definition of, 336-337
  description of, 337-347
Hysterics, 153
Idealist, 44
Idiots, 83, 103
Imbecile, 103
Impulse, as element of personality, 18
  character formation in setting goals for, 305-311
  definition of, 21, 78-79, 303-305
  differentiation of from instinct, 83-84
  ego in relation to strength of, 313
  evolutionary basis of, 78
  goals of, 303-305
  immature, 110
  influence on ego strength, 216
  life, 82
  sex at puberty, 319-324
    development of, 319-324
    deviation of, 326, 330-336
    immaturity of, 326, 333-335
    strong, 91
    weak, 91
  strength, conservation of, 314-315
    evaluation of, 312-317
    of, 311-312
    of and physical vigor, 311
  sublimation of, 314-318
  suppression of, 315-316
  temperament in relation to strength of, 312-313
  weak, 91
Inner tension, 138, 148
Insane, disadvantages of term, 41
Insight, 177
  into anxious mood, 204
  into temperament, 130-131

Instinct, advantages and disadvantages of, 84-88
  definition of, 83-84
  in birds, 85
  in human beings, 89
  in insects, 85
Intelligence, 21-22, 78, 82-83, 87, 91, 101-102, 104
  as an element of personality, 18
  hereditary, basis of, 103
  high, 123
  low, 83, 106, 108, 110, 123, 125
  manifestations of, 102-103
  measure of, 103
  place of, 103
  views regarding, 109
Intelligentsia, 109
Invention, 69
Irritable, cases of, 175-181
  contrasted with explosive, 174-175
  definition of, 140
  description of, 173-181
  lack of judgment, 174-175, 180
Irritability, control of, 177-181
  from low oxygen, 135-136
  in relation to tempo, 188
  of old age, 175
  of sensitive, 248-249

Job, 261
John Bull, 35, 38

Lawyer, trial, 69, 72
Leaders, 70
Leptosome. See leptosomic physique
Leptosomic physique, description of, 18, 42-43, 45-46, 51, 55, 108
Lincoln, Abraham, 70
Locke, John, 70-71
Louis XIV, 249

Machiavelli, 229

Mania, 58
Manic-depressive, form of mental illness, description of, 56-63
  mild. *See* hypomanic
  nature of, 41, 43
Marat, 97
Martyrs, 261
Melancholy, 58
Menopause, influence of on mood, 136
Menstruation, influence of on mood, 136
Mental illness, manic-depressive, 56-63
  paranoid, 296-299
  significance of symptoms, 43
Mimics, 148
Mirabeau, Honoré, 71-74
Misers, 228
Mood, anxious. *See* anxious
  change of. *See* mood-swings
  cheerful, description of, 187-212
  description of, 22, 133-138, 187-212
  fundamental, 134-138
    alteration of by disease, 134-136
  gloomy, description of, 189-194
  irritable. *See* irritable
  relation to tempo, 188
Mood-swings, description of, 51-52, 55, 208-212
  in relation to food, 209
  pyknic physique, 51-52, 55
Moody, description of, 208-212
Moron, 103, 123
Mussolini, 97
Myxedema, 138-139

Napoleon, 113
Narcissism, 334-335
Nervous breakdown, 63
Normal man, contrasted with excitable, 152-153

Normal man—(*Continued*)
  definition of, viii-ix, 97, 141
  ego evaluation of, 219-225

Œdipus complex, 263
Old age, irritability of, 175
Organizers, 69
Paranoia, 296-299
Personality, adaptability of, 95
  and physique, 37-74
  basic traits, permanency of, 8, 13-14
  compensation for deviation in, 107-108, 349
  complexity of, 82
  definition of, 13
  descriptive, classification of, 11-12
  designation of, 348-349
  deviations in, 97
  disturbances of, 100
  elements of, 15-18
  evolutionary development of, 77-89
  fanatical, 348
  "flabby" fanatical, 348
  heredity in establishment of traits of, 91-95
  hypochondriacal, 348
  hysterical. *See* hysterical personality
  influence of on character formation, 91-95
  integration of structure, 335-336
  interrelation of parts, 105
  normal, definition of, 97
  permanency of traits, 92
  psychopathic, 37, 97-99
  revealed through behavior, 14
  structural analysis, end result, 348-350
Phlegmatic, description of, 181-187
  mood in, 186
Phlegmatism, degrees of, 186

INDEX

Phobias, 205-207
Phrenology, 53
Physical disease in relation to physique, 38-40
symptoms, psychic origin of, 100-101
Physician, 69
Physique and personality, relation between 19, 37-74
as an element of personality, 18
athletic, 46-47, 49
dysplastic, 50-51
habitus apoplepticus, 38
phthysicus, 38
in relation to physical disease, 38-40
leptosomic, 19, 45-46, 51
pyknic, 19, 42-46, 50, 55, 69
in relation to mood-swings, 51-52, 55
Pickwick, 45
Plato, 3-4, 7-12, 16, 19-25, 28-29
Poe, Edgar Allan, 190
Poets, 70-71
Political theorists, 71
Politician, 69
Premonition, 200
Prestige as goal. *See* egocentric
Psychoanalysis, 280-281
Psychoneurosis, 100-101, 115, 341
Psychopathic behavior, 98-101, 105-106, 108
personality, definition of, 97-99
Puberty, 319-321
Puritans, 35
Pyknic, physique of, 42-46, 50, 55, 69
description of, 44-45
relation to mood-swings, 51-52, 55

Quacks, 101
Quarrelsome, 181

Racial types in physique, 35

Realist, 20, 44
Realities, comprehension of, 19-20, 64, 67
Religion, regard of, 20, 260
Resentful, case of, 271-275, 277-283
description of, 268-283
lack of adjustment, 269-271, 275
social judgment, 275-277
Resonance and cheerful mood, 189
gloomy mood, 193
influence of on personality, 22-24, 133
Restlessness, 110
Robespierre, 72
Roosevelt, Theodore, 71-72, 74
Rousseau, 72

St. Anthony, 316
Salesman, 69
Santa Claus, 34, 36
Schizophrenic, form of mental illness, description of, 64-68
nature of, 41-44
Scolding, 108
Security, maintenance of, 9
Self-advancement, struggle for, 124
-consciousness, 156, 255-256
in relation to egoist, 268
-evaluation, 10-11
-improvement, requirements for, 349-350
-pity of sensitive, 285-286
-reference of sensitive, 291-299
Sensitive, cases of, 287-296
description of, 283-300
gloomy mood, 284
irritability of, 248-249
paranoid tendency of, 296-299
reaction to criticism, 287-292
self-pity of, 285-286
-reference of, 291-299
sense of persecution of, 291-299
Sensitivity, 255-256

INDEX

Sex education, importance of, 325-326
  false goals of, 324
  impulse at puberty, 319-321
    definition of, 317-318
    development of, 319-324
    deviation of, 326, 330-333
    immaturity of, 326, 333-335
    over-evaluation of, 318-319
Sexual differentiation, anatomical, 326-330
  psychological, 329-330
  goals, pseudo, 322-323
  impotency and anxious mood, 208
  selection, influence of fashion on, 55-56
Shakespeare, 34
Sublimation of impulse, 314-317
Submissive, description of, 259-268
Suffocation, sensation of, 201

Tea, effect of on mood, 136
Temperament as an element of personality, 18, 22, 78, 83
  centered in thalamus, 81
  definition of, 129-132
  excitable, 151-161
  explosive, 140, 161-172
  group, 80-81
  hereditary endowment, 129-130
  in lower animals, 79
  in relation to strength of impulse, 312-313
  insight into, 130-131
  irritable, 173-181
  peculiarities of as cause of psychopathic behavior, 140
  permanency of qualities of, 129-130
  See also, mood, temperament, resonance, emotive, vivacious, excitable, irritable, phlegmatic, torpid, anxious, mood-swings, phobias
  tempo of, 136
  vivacious, 141-151

Temper-tantrum, 161
Tempo in relation to cheerfulness, 188
  irritability, 188
  of temperament, 133, 136
Tension, inner, 137
Thalamus, 81
Theophrastus, 3-4, 7-12, 16, 19-25, 28, 29
  "characters" of, 3-4, 7-12, 16, 19-25, 28, 29
  types chosen, 8-10
  fallacy in classification, 8, 11
Theorists, 69
Thyroid gland, 138-139
Timidity, 255-256
Tobacco, effect of on excitable, 160
  mood, 136
Trial lawyer, 69, 72
Tuberculosis, 38-40

Uncle Sam, 35, 38

Vivacious, cases of, 142-147
  contrasted with anxious, 148
  excitable, 152
  explosive, 161
  irritable, 148-151
  description of, 140-151
  effects of alcohol on, 151
  resonance of, 151
Vulgarity, 26

Weak ego and martyrdom, 261-263
  cases of, 261-267
  description of, 253-255
  in relation to religion, 260-261
  resentful. See resentful
  sensitive. See sensitive
  submissive. See submissive
  type of, 259
Weak impulse, 94
William the Conqueror, 244
Wilson, Woodrow, 72, 74